REDSKIN TRAIL

The tribe had now found her name. She was "the Woman who prays always".

A Life of
BLESSED PHILIPPINE DUCHESNE

———✠———

REDSKIN TRAIL

by

M. K. RICHARDSON

with illustrations by
"ROBIN"

LONDON
BURNS OATES

NIHIL OBSTAT: GEORGIVS SMITH, S.T.D., PH.D.
CENSOR DEPVTATVS
IMPRIMATVR: E. MORROGH BERNARD
VICARIVS GENERALIS
WESTMONASTERII: DIE XXIV APRILIS MCMLI

MADE AND PRINTED IN GREAT BRITAIN
BY THE BROADWATER PRESS LTD, WELWYN GARDEN CITY
FOR BURNS OATES & WASHBOURNE LTD
28 ASHLEY PLACE, LONDON, S.W.1
First published 1952

Contents

Contents

Illustrations

vii

Introduction

IN August 1769 were born Napoleon Bonaparte and Rose Philippine Duchesne. In both the spirit of world conquest was strong, but the Emperor was already a defeated and dying man when the obscure nun was just beginning the work for which God had destined her. Masterful, natural gifts had to be supernaturalized and refined before the kingdoms of this world could be brought under the reign of Christ without the disaster that wrecked the Empire. The way in which the traditional Duchesne character, compounded of strength and wilfulness, was made an instrument of value in the hands of God is fully described in the pages of Blessed Philippine Duchesne's first biographer, Mgr Baunard.[1] A more complete understanding of the American scene is to be found in Marjorie Erskine's *Mother Philippine Duschesne* (Longmans, 1926), in Louise Callan's *The Society of the Sacred Heart in North America* (Longmans, 1937) and in Margaret Williams's *The Second Sowing* (Sheed and Ward, 1942). Blessed Philippine wrote an account of her early life, and some of her letters are extant, together with the diary kept of the voyage from Bordeaux to St Louis. The faithful, impersonal records kept by her of the first American foundations reveal the writer's character as do the letters written to her by Ste Madeleine Sophie, Fr Louis Barat, Fr Varin and many others who worked with her. Incidents in her life and fragments of her conversation were noted down by priests, nuns, seculars, and children, and subse-

[1] *Histoire de Madame Duchesne*, Paris, 1879.

I

quently retold in a variety of written reminiscences. All give testimony to a vital personality refined through the years by her burning love of God.

In retelling her story, fictitious detail has only been used to expand an incomplete factual sketch, as when Mother Hardy in recording the story of how Blessed Philippine Duchesne bathed the face of a negro who had been struck by his master omitted to give the reason for the blow. Characters playing minor parts have been built up on hints, though the majority of the chief actors have words and deeds duly chronicled at length. The greatest liberty with fact is the creation of the de Saussure family. Mgr Baunard discreetly speaks of the arrangement of a marriage by the parents, but omits the name of the young man. On the model of most French alliances, he was probably the son of a family well known to the Duchesnes and of the same social standing. Some of his remarks and those of his daughter were actually made by contemporaries and by the children at Ste Marie d'en Haut, but otherwise the de Saussure family belongs to the realm of possibility rather than actuality. They seemed useful as a source of comment, as did Little Owl at Sugar Creek. A good deal of dialogue is genuine reported speech. Sometimes what was written has been used as though spoken. But this is not meant to be a source book and, if literal fact is wanted, the other lives should be consulted.

When Mother Duchesne died, a short notice appeared in a Missouri paper. Fr de Smet wrote: "The dry announcement of her death truly vexed me. No greater saint ever died in Missouri or perhaps in the whole Union." It was in keeping with her life that her Beatification should have taken place on 12 May 1940, in a world torn by war, with the heritage of Christian centuries crumbling beneath bombs and consumed by fire. But the lesson of her great-hearted, selfless example shone out the more clearly. May some of the missionary fire that burnt in the soul of Blessed Philippine Duchesne, urging her to conquer the whole world for Christ, inflame Catholics now to work among the savages of our modern times.

1: *Bread on the Waters*

THE stone parapet of the bridge was hot beneath the priest's elbows. Below, the swift waters of the Isère coming down from the snows sent up a hint of coolness, but the peaks of the mountains were lost in the heat haze and the sun shone from a cloudless sky over a drowsy town. In a niche on the opposite side of the bridge a beggar lay asleep. His half-opened mouth showed black and broken teeth, his bare feet, sticking out from the mass of rags that covered him, were dirty and ulcerous. But he slept unconcerned, and unconcerned the few folk astir on that summer afternoon passed him by.

"Strange," the priest mused, "how little we realize our own ills or the ills of others. I might be living in another world from the one that gives me my life's work. Grenoble—America. There are more than thousands of miles of land and sea separating them. What am I doing here? Those fat, comfortable market women haggling down there over the price of a hen—do they really breathe the same air as my redskins gliding like snakes through the bushes to gain the scalp of their enemy? The good housewives of the bankers and prosperous business men who entertain me here are perturbed if the seasoning of a dish goes wrong—and in my country I must beware of cannibalism. There are churches here at everyone's door, the sacraments within everyone's reach—it's like speaking a strange language

3

if I try to explain life in primeval forests and virgin prairies with never a priest at hand, and souls that Christ died for dying in their thousands without hearing of His Blessed Name. What am I doing here but wasting my time? Better go back and labour in the harvest while I still have strength."

A bell rang out from a convent on the farther hillside. He sighed. "Ste Marie d'en Haut. There'll be good Visitation nuns praying there, worrying over their own shortcomings and quietly cleaning their souls like brushing specks from butterflies' wings. What would they think if I could tell them of the horrors that are done in my parish? Gentle St Francis of Sales might not like it if an unruly son of St Ignatius broke into the calm of his daughters with tales of crime and passion and cruelty and martyrdom. Would it spur them to greater prayer? Would it inspire some to live out their name and be truly nuns of the Visitation of America? Ah, well, they live their lives as God wills them to, and I, please God, try to do His good pleasure in the mission field. Yet how white is the harvest, and how few the labourers!"

"Don't be silly!"

A boy's voice interrupted his reverie, and he turned round. A few paces from him a small girl and two boys were arguing.

"You've only got a sou left," the taller boy said. "I bet he doesn't need it."

"You can't give it to him," the first speaker went on.

"Can't I!"

The girl turned her back on the boys and marched across the road. She stopped in front of the beggar and looked at him. The rags rose and fell with his heavy breathing. Then she put out her hand and shook him.

"Here's something for you," she said as he roused with a grunt.

He took the coin, mumbled his thanks, spat and settled himself once more. Back across the road the boys still remonstrated.

"You shouldn't throw away your money like that. You're

"You shouldn't throw away your money. . . . You're always giving it to poor people."

always giving it to poor people. Your mother and father give it you for your own little pleasures."

The priest saw the child's head go up with a determined tilt.

"Well, it's my pleasure to spend it like this."

The older boy laughed but as they moved over the bridge towards the town, the younger one was protesting:

"It's silly, that's what it is."

"Silly. Silly to waste money on the down-and-outs. France has her problems as well as America," thought the priest. "All very well for Grenoble with her wealthy manufacturers and exporters of textiles, and her independent parliament able to defy the King in Paris. But France herself, on the verge of bankruptcy, rotten with evil living and yet more rotten with the philosophical ideas that would do away with all religion—what of her? Can the King do anything after the long lax reign of his grandfather? Has he the wits or the character? And what help can he get from his wife? Three years of queening it, and Marie Antoinette is the same beautiful, ill-educated, high-spirited, selfish girl as when she married Louis. I should be tempted to take the road yonder up over the mountain and through the woods to the Grande Chartreuse to escape from this artificial life of gaiety on the edge of a precipice, to break through the changing things of time into the Carthusian's contemplation of the eternal, unchanging truths of God, did I not know the stark realities of life in the colonies. Grenoble sleeping to-day in the shimmering heat—it's like a painted picture. Strange if I suddenly saw the dip of paddles and the war canoes of my Indians approaching up the Isère. Life cutting through the canvas."

The Jesuit stood up straight and brushed the dust of the parapet from his threadbare sleeve.

"I must smarten myself before I visit M. Duchesne," he thought, and rubbed a stain from his cuff. He felt in his pocket for his handkerchief and his fingers closed on something hard.

"The bread I meant to feed the birds with," he thought with a smile. "It's too stale now to offer the beggar."

He pitched it over the bridge into the swirling water and watched it sink.

"Cast your bread upon the waters," he said ironically to himself. "Well, I shan't see that again. Now for an evening of talking pious nothings to unimaginative women, and politics with their husbands who see all the world from the angle of France."

He crossed the bridge into the town. The air was close, but the tall stone houses gave shade. He paused and looked at the distant towers of the monastery of the Minims.

"There lies the body of Bayard, that knight without fear and without reproach. Where lies his spirit? Is it lost to Dauphiné and to France?"

A woman standing in a doorway called to him.

"You're wanting something?"

"Yes. The house of the Duchesnes."

"You've not far to go. See the Church of St André down there? Well, it's just opposite; you can't miss it—close to the old palace of the Counts of Dauphiné."

He went on. The house he sought in the Place St André was stern and uninviting. Grated windows seemed there to shut out the world and to shut in those who dwelt there. The big outer door opened to him and he found himself in a covered passage that led into a severe looking courtyard whence a great stairway led him at length into the apartments of M. Duchesne. The servant who showed him the way threw wide the door. At once the priest was aware of something different from his expectations. The room seemed full of life. There were children, boys and girls, laughing together, while their elders were talking with animation. M. Pierre Duchesne, a well-set-up man, came forward with a smile, and made the introductions.

"My wife, my brother-in-law, Claude Périer; Mme Périer will be here in a minute. Our houses are united by masonry as well as love. Camille, run and tell your mother that our visitor has come. We've built a passage between the houses; it lets all the children meet together easily. They're a good crowd, aren't they?" he said, glancing round at the boys and girls, now silent, waiting in the background. The cousins were presented one by one.

"The boys are my responsibility," said M. Périer with a wry smile. "This little one is my sister's."

The priest found himself looking down at the child he had watched on the bridge.

"This is Rose Philippine," Mme Duchesne said. "Just eight to-day."

"The vigil of St Rose of Lima's feast," the priest commented. "That's why they called you Rose?"

The child nodded.

"But I was baptized on Our Lady's birthday," she said proudly.

"And what do you know about your patron—the first flower of holiness to blossom in the New World—my world, you know."

"She slept on broken crockery and had a piece of wood for her pillow," Rose Philippine answered.

"You're not going to imitate her and cut off all your hair?" the priest asked.

Mme Duchesne interrupted.

"No need for her to do that. She lost all her good looks through having smallpox when she was three. You've nothing to be vain about, have you, Philippine?"

"No," the child replied with simple acceptance of a truth. The priest took in the well-marked features, the high colour of the face, the mass of fair hair and the blue eyes.

"Not a beauty *à la* Pompadour or *à la* Marie Antoinette," he thought, "but there's beauty there in spite of the smallpox. And what do you know of your other patron?" he asked aloud.

"Oh, St Philip—he was the Apostle, you know, the one that met the Ethiopian and baptized him," Philippine answered quickly. "Do you baptize people too in the New World—they said you were a missionary?"

"Do you track down Red Indians with tomahawks?" one

of the Périer boys asked. "Can you tell us tales about Fr Jogues and Fr de Brébœuf and Fr Lallemant?"

"They belonged to the north," the priest answered. "I come from further south, from Louisiana. But there have been martyrs there too."

"Tell us—" the boys were eager but Mme Périer entered at that moment and the talk moved on to other topics. M. Duchesne wanted to know how the French settlers viewed the revolt of the English colonists against taxation from the Mother Country. How would the text of the American Declaration of Independence affect public opinion among the southern French planters? Would negro labour be available if the Rights of Man were accepted in their full implications, M. Périer asked, and how would that affect the supply of cotton for the textile industries? The children bided their time, but when wine and sweet biscuits were brought in and the conversation veered to the vintage and the state of agriculture in France, they returned to the charge.

"But if I tell you true stories," the priest objected, "it may frighten the girls. Mlle Philippine won't like to hear of tortures and bloodshed." Again he caught the determined tilt of the head.

"It's all right, Father," said Philippine, "I'm reading the lives of the early Christian martyrs and there are plenty of tortures in them."

M. Duchesne shrugged his shoulders.

"Give them all the horrors they're longing for," he said. "They must learn that the world is not all junkets and cream."

It was a spellbound audience that listened to his tales. He told them how Fr Rasles had converted the fierce tribe of the Abnakis and had tamed their savage nature. Together they had raised a cross to remind them of their gentle Saviour. Then came the day when a band of Indians with three English officers had attacked their camp. At the foot of the cross they had seized the Jesuit, shot him, scalped him and cut him in pieces.

B

Then there was the tribe of the Natchez. Fr du Poisson had laboured among them despite the cruelties they wrought on him, until at length they cut off his head. Fr Souel had been shot. His poor cassock, stained red with his blood, had been torn from his body and borne about as a banner by the wild hordes who slew him. Then came the thrilling story of Fr Doutreleau saying his Mass on the river bank when the alarm came and he fled, still wearing his vestments, to a canoe while shots were fired at him from every side. As he spoke, the priest was aware of two members of his audience who listened in a special way to him. The little girl Philippine gazed steadily at him, as though her bright blue eyes saw the maple woods reddening in the Indian summer, the canoes sweeping along over the rapids, and the great silent peaks of the Rockies beyond and beyond, beckoning the missioners onwards in spirit though their bodies were hacked in pieces before they had reached that goal. In the background of the group, M. Duchesne sat with his keen law-yer's face half hidden in the hand that supported his forehead. From time to time a faint smile flickered across his face.

"He cares nothing for the souls of Indians," thought the priest, and rather lamely finished a tale of sacrilege perpetrated by the savages.

"Terrible, terrible," Mme Duchesne said.

"All is for the best in the best possible of worlds," her husband remarked dryly.

"So that's it," the priest thought. "He follows Voltaire. I have wasted my time in speaking of the missions."

The boys clamoured for more, but he excused himself. It was time to go. Philippine stood up with a deep sigh, but the priest had moved off with his host.

"I am going out," said M. Duchesne and took him to the door that led into the Place St André. The evening had grown cooler, but as they stepped into the roadway together, the priest felt the same sense of walking into an unreal world.

"We part company here," said M. Duchesne. "I am going into the town to discuss philosophy."

"And I back to the presbytery the other side of the river," said the priest.

"Very different roads," M. Duchesne answered. "Ah, well, we must each cultivate our garden."

He bowed and walked off. For a minute or two the priest stood in the square. A couple of fat pigeons were pecking among the garbage in the gutter. He felt in his pocket for the crust of bread.

"I forgot—I threw it away in the water," he said.

2: Sapling Oak

FRÉDÉRIC de Saussure's mother saw to it that her son was well dressed when Mme Duchesne and her daughters came to call.

"Euphrosyne Périer was very well off before she married Pierre François Duchesne," she remarked to her husband. "And now he's a coming man. They are all speaking of his ability at the bar, and, mark my words, he'll be leading Parliament in a very short time. Amélie is too old, but Philippine would make a good match for our Frédéric."

"He'll need it," sighed General de Saussure. "I haven't exactly made a fortune in the army. I wouldn't want to marry a Duchesne—they are too energetic for me—and I should wager that little one has a good temper—but what's the good of my talking? You ladies will fix the affair to your own liking. At any rate, it won't be for some years. They're only twelve, after all."

Frédéric was glad that the Périer boys were not coming. They would want to do things—and that might spoil the set of his cravat and untidy his hair, which was neatly caught back by a narrow black ribbon. His plum-coloured velvet suit gave him a certain confidence to meet the girls. He needed confidence, though he would not admit even to himself that Philippine always gave him a sense of inferiority. She had a way of looking straight at him that was disconcerting. But she was interesting to talk to. She did not bother about dress and silly idle gossip like other girls whom he had to play with. He waited patiently on one of his mother's spindly, gilt-backed chairs, thinking, "I'll show her that old copy of Ronsard's poems I found in the library."

Mme Duchesne was announced. Amélie and Philippine followed in her wake. Greetings over, by tacit agreement the mothers disposed of the children in order to talk together.

"Frédéric, wouldn't you like to take Mlles Amélie and Philippine to the library?" Mme de Saussure said, leaving him no chance of not liking.

He rose obediently, and led the way.

"Philippine is fond of reading," he heard Mme Duchesne remark.

"Such a good thing—Frédéric is a real bookworm," his mother was saying as he closed the door.

"Come along," he said. "I've a lovely book of poems to show you."

Amélie smothered a yawn. Philippine went forward eagerly, but forgot about Frédéric's book as soon as they entered the library. On the table a large map of France lay open.

"Let's find where we are," she suggested.

She and Frédéric sprawled over the table.

"There's Lyons," she said. "I've often been there."

"Well, it's no distance," he said, putting her in her place. "I've been much further. Look, here's us, here's Grenoble and there's the Isère, and if you go all down it, you come to the Rhône, and then you go on and you come to Avignon. That's what I did with my father last year. It was nice to see the Palace of the Popes but I liked Arles and Nîmes much better. There were some awfully interesting Roman ruins and things there."

"Philippine would have liked that," Amélie put in. "She used to be mad on Roman History. When I was ill a couple of years ago, she tried to amuse me by reading Roman History to me."

Amélie laughed. The colour mounted to Philippine's face and she bit her lip.

"I thought you would like it," she said. "I did."

"You're not everybody," her sister said.

Frédéric went on boasting.

"And then we went on to Marseilles, and we took a sailing boat over to Corsica and it was ever so exciting."

"Were there bandits lurking in the undergrowth?" Amélie asked. "I wouldn't want to go there. I'd be afraid I was going to have a knife stuck in me."

"Of course it's all right there." Frédéric could be superior even to the older girl. "Corsicans aren't all bandits. I met a jolly interesting boy from there and he wasn't a bit of a bandit—he was as French as you or me. His father had gone as a sort of ambassador to Versailles. His name was Bonaparte."

"A boy," said Amélie. "You wait until he's grown up."

"He was quite grown up—as old as me," said Frédéric huffily.

"And when were you born?" asked Amélie.

"Seventeen sixty-nine, so you see he was nearly twelve. That's the same age as Philippine."

"Ah, well, where did you meet him—in Ajaccio?"

"No, it was in Brienne when I went to the military academy there with my father. Bonaparte was going to be a cadet there."

"They must have begun to tame him already," said Amélie, "so that doesn't count. I still wouldn't like to go to Corsica."

"All right. Let's look at the book I found——" Frédéric tried to turn the subject, but Philippine had her hand between the pages of the atlas.

"I want to look at America," she said, and found the place. Amélie yawned again and turned to the bookshelves. Frédéric had to give way. He always did, with this Duchesne girl. She was running her finger over the surface of the map.

"What's wrong with your fingers?" he asked, looking at red swellings on them.

"Chilblains," said Philippine, with her thoughts on the New World.

"My mother makes me put oil on my hands and wraps them up in silk," said the boy. "I can't write properly if I get chilblains."

"Nor can I," said Philippine, "but it doesn't matter. Mother says we've got to learn not to be soft with ourselves. The early martyrs weren't."

"They did a lot of silly things," Frédéric objected. "And anyhow, I don't believe half those stories. How do people know what they did?"

"Well, then, the French martyrs in America weren't soft."

"I've read some of their 'Relations'," said Frédéric, trying to assert himself again. He was pleased to see this made an impression on his guest. He pointed to the map.

"Look, the explorers following Jacques Cartier came down the St Lawrence. Champlain founded Quebec on the Rock in 1608 and then went on to discover Lake Ontario and the Ottawa valley and Lake Superior."

"That's where the Jesuits went—I know all about their dying," said Philippine. "It doesn't look very far on the map from Louisiana."

"It's thousands and thousands of miles," Frédéric informed her. "Look, see the Ohio river here. Well, that's where Robert Cavalier, Sieur de la Salle, started from—he knew all about the Jesuits, too, because he'd been brought up by them—and he went all down the river, all along the Mississippi—the Indians call it the Father of Waters—and it took him months and months and months—and at last he got to the sea and he said all the land ought to belong to France and so he called it Louisiana after King Louis XIV and the soldiers all shot off their muskets and called out, 'Long live the King!' And after that, French people settled there."

"And that's when the priests began converting the Indians down in the south," Philippine said.

"I expect so," Frédéric answered. He found that part a bit
boring. "I think it's awfully sad that it doesn't belong to us
now."

Their two heads bent over the map.

"There's nothing left now," said Philippine. "The English
took Canada from us when Montcalm died at Quebec and
Louisiana was taken by Spain when the Treaty of Paris was
signed in 1763. Father told me."

"We could have bought it back again, my father says, if
only we weren't stony broke. He says we'll never get straight
now that Necker has been dismissed."

"Who's he?" Philippine asked.

"Oh, a banker—like your uncle—I don't understand about
money but I think he was making the king economize. Anyhow, I'd much rather we fought to get it back. I don't mean
me—but soldiers, really good soldiers. That's what that Corsican boy said. It's prestige we want."

"What's that?" asked Philippine.

"Oh, people looking up to you so that when you say you'll
do a thing, they think you will."

"But when I say a thing, I do always mean to do it," Philippine said. "Don't you?"

Frédéric avoided the answer.

"See that musket hanging on the wall there? Well, that's
the new one they're arming all the infantry with. My father
laughs at it. That's because it's made on a Prussian model and
he can't bear the Prussians. But that boy I told you of said it was
the very finest thing out. He said it was time there were real
soldiers in the army and not just play-acting ones dressed up in
gorgeous uniforms to be present at court functions. I think
that's all my father does, you know. You can't fight and win if
you aren't serious over it. And you must have good artillery,
he said, and you must have troops that can move quickly without a lot of baggage and stuff. I bet if he was grown up now,
he'd get back our colonies."

"Then the Jesuits would be able to go right up the Mississippi and the Missouri and right over the whole continent to the Rocky Mountains," said Philippine.

"Oh, I expect so," the boy replied carelessly. "Aren't you coming to look at my Ronsard?"

"No, I want to look at this map still."

She pored over it while he grew sulky. If only his mother had not made him promise to be polite. There she was getting her own way again. He wanted to say out loud to her, "It's a jolly good name you've got—Du Chesne—you're just about as hard and unbending as an oak tree. I want you to come with me, but you won't budge from what you want to do."

Fortunately Amélie sensed something wrong and came across to them.

"Let's go back to mother," she said.

In the drawing-room, the two ladies had had their chat.

"I've been telling Mme de Saussure that we are sending you to school to-morrow to Ste Marie d'en Haut," Mme Duchesne said, drawing Philippine against her knee.

"I wish they had allowed the Jesuits to keep their colleges," sighed Mme de Saussure. "Frédéric has a mind worth cultivating."

"Oh, it's to prepare her for her First Holy Communion really that we are sending Philippine there," said Mme Duchesne.

"Good," thought Frédéric. "She won't be coming here for ages and making me do what she wants."

When they said goodbye, he went and had a good look at himself in his plum-coloured velvet suit. He really did have a distinguished air in it. The sort of air that would give you prestige. That would make other people do what you wanted when you said it. That is, if they didn't happen to be Duchesnes.

3: Grafting

THE whole household was there when the carriage came to take Philippine off to Ste Marie d'en Haut. M. Duchesne kissed her tenderly on both cheeks.

"Work hard and use your intelligence," he said, and then, as the eager blue eyes still sought his, he added, lamely enough, "and learn your catechism well. Religion is a great help to women. It has made your mother the good wife she is."

That was all. With a stab of disappointment she turned to kiss Amélie. Her younger sister Charlotte hugged her and so did Marie Périer, while the boys, all eight of them, counting the baby in arms, waved goodbye. Mme Duchesne was waiting for her in the carriage.

"Now, no tears, Philippine," she said as she climbed in. "And sit up straight."

They drove through the streets of the city and over the bridge. When the road began to climb steeply, Mme Duchesne stopped the carriage.

"Wait for me here," she told the driver, and set off on foot with her daughter.

"We are taking the same road as two great saints a century and a half ago. Can't you imagine St Francis of Sales and St Jane de Chantal seeing the sharp, bleak heights of Rabot lying behind this mountain side and deciding that they would buy the ground and make the fourth convent of the Visitation here—you'll find all kinds of remembrances of them in the building. And of Duchesnes too. Quite a number of them became nuns here or in other Visitation convents."

Philippine was silent. Her heart was heavy and the houses on each side of the steep street were dismal and looked as though they might fall to pieces any moment. A sudden turn, and they were facing an archway.

"Here we are," said Madame Duchesne and went forward. Philippine felt that the arch was formidable. It cut off the familiar landscape of home and family and noisy cousins, and led her to something dark and unknown. But she was coming here to make her First Communion. God was waiting for her. She quickened her step and caught up her mother, who had already rung the bell. The door of the convent was opening. A dark corridor stretched before them. Dark, but there seemed sunlight at the end of it. The sister led them along it, and they came to a cloistered square in which green grass and bright flowers grew and there was a sparkling white stone cross, and above, the depths of the sky.

"These steps lead down to the nuns' choir," said the sister, and as she spoke, Reverend Mother de Murinais emerged and greeted them. There were explanations, recommendations, exchange of compliments. It was hard to take everything in. Another nun waited in the background. At length the time came for parting.

"This is Mother Latier de Bayanne, who has special charge of the pupils," the Reverend Mother was saying. "There are twenty of them, so your daughter will not feel lonely."

As if numbers mattered when you were without the company of those you loved! Philippine found her mother's arms round her.

"I know you will be good, my dear, and prepare yourself for the great day to come. Not the smallest little spot or shadow on your soul. Pray and mortify yourself. Be careful and watchful. Nothing soiled can enter heaven. Your aunt and I will come for your first meeting with our Eucharistic Lord."

"And Father?" Philippine faltered.

"I think he will be too busy," said her mother. "Pray for him."

Then she was gone and Philippine was alone with strangers.

"Don't be afraid, child," said Mother de Bayanne. "I'll show you round and then you'll feel better. Let's go into the chapel first."

"Why, it's as big as a church!" said Philippine, standing by the open door.

"The marble altar is very fine," said her guide, but Philippine was looking instead at the statues on each side of the altar. On the left stood Our Lord, His breast bared to show His Sacred Heart burning with love for men, His wound-imprinted Hand pointing to It for all to know His meaning. On the right was St Francis of Sales holding in his outstretched hand a burning heart, his own offered in exchange.

"That's what I want to do," thought Philippine. "Just that, when He gives me His Heart."

"Do you see the symbol of the Sacred Heart in the marble of the altar?" said Mother de Bayanne. "It's on the arch of the sanctuary and in the pavement. If you look up to the roof, you'll see frescoes of the mysteries of the Gospel. Come outside. All these pictures along this passage are meant to remind us of God's goodness to us, right from the very first moment of creation all through the ages until He gave Himself in the Bread and Wine of the Last Supper. And here, the very last one of all, just at the chapel door, is the one that He told Sister Margaret Mary Alacoque to have painted at Paray-le-Monial —His Sacred Heart wounded and on fire, with the cross rising from the crown of thorns that encircles it."

"There's something written there," said Philippine, and bending forward, she read: "He was wounded for our iniquities."

Our iniquities. Her mother's last counsels came back to her. There were to be no iniquities in her when the great day came.

Ste Marie des Hauts

"Let's go into the chapel first"
"Why, it's as big as a church!" said Philippine.

It was all very awesome. A little terrifying when you knew you had a temper.

"You've not read the other text," said the nun. "Go right up to it."

"You shall draw waters with joy out of the Saviour's fountains," Philippine read. That was a different thought. She hardly listened when the nun pointed out the confessional used by St Francis or the stall and prie-dieu of St Jane. Other thoughts were too big and insistent.

"It's all Our Lord's Sacred Heart here," she said at length.

"Well, even before He showed Sister Margaret Mary how He wanted to be loved, He had made our founder and foundress understand it. When you are older, you can read what St Francis writes time and again about It. He says, 'The dying Saviour has given birth to us in the opening of His Sacred Heart,' and St Jane said once, 'If we are very humble and very faithful, we shall have the Heart of our crucified Lord as our abode and resting-place in this world and our everlasting habitation in His heavenly palace!' Now come and see your companions."

They were all very kind to her, though they found she was not over eager to go about arm in arm with them, or talk about the good and bad points of the nuns who looked after them or those they saw in choir. She joined the few who were preparing for their First Communion and wasted no time over her work.

"She's a very serious-minded child," said Mother Marie Delphine, who helped with the scholars. "She always seems to be in the chapel and kneeling so still in front of the altar."

Mother de Bayanne shrugged her shoulders.

"Yet I'm sure she's got a sense of humour hidden away somewhere. She can make some very pointed remarks. And if she's serious, well, that's maybe because she's got real faith, and realizes more than most of them what she is preparing for. Besides, she's probably a bit homesick as yet."

It was one day on the terrace where the pupils had their playground that Philippine's feeling of strangeness suddenly vanished. Mother de Bayanne was beside her, pointing to the roofs of the town below, with the silver river running at the foot of the hill.

"You see how convenient this would have been if we had really done what St Francis meant us to do, and visited the poor and sick. This would have been like a kind of eagle's nest from which we could have watched and flown down and then returned in safety to be with God. But the times weren't ripe for that kind of work and so we've grilles and enclosure and the only visiting we do is with our prayers."

She moved off but Philippine turned over the idea. A nest. Birds were secure in their nests, their homes. And eagles. They were birds of the mountains. She lifted her eyes and saw rising all round her mountain after mountain, till on the horizon the snow-peaks showed white. The mountains of God. How beautiful! She could fly like an eagle with unblinking eyes into the mountains of God, as Mother de Bayanne had said, in prayer. She realized in a flash that she was at home in this eyrie.

Mother de Bayanne talked about eagles again in her instruction to the First Communicants in the next week.

"You must all be eagles and soar high—not little sparrows chirping about fussily in the dust," she said. "You must be great and strong."

"Eagles are the Kings of Birds, aren't they?" one girl asked. "Is that why emperors choose them for their standards?"

"They're grasping," another girl objected. "I mean, they swoop down on what they want and they put their claws into it and keep it. I think they are rather frightening."

"I like the way they go up and up," said Philippine. "But they have got talons, it's true."

"Well," said Mother de Bayanne, "an eagle is the symbol of St John the Evangelist, the Apostle who leaned against the Sacred Heart, so I expect there's a way of getting rid of the claws."

"How?" asked Philippine.

"Suppose I change the parable by taking the passage of St

John's own gospel," said Mother de Bayanne. "He tells us how Our Lord at the Last Supper called Himself the Vine and we the branches. You know that when there's a tree that can't grow properly by itself, it is sometimes taken and grafted on another one. Something like that happens to us when we are baptized. We are like wild trees, or too delicate fruit trees, or too stubborn oaks, but we are grafted into the Great Vine and the sap from it runs through our branches and in the end we become like it. That is what Holy Communion does for us—it keeps giving us that lifegiving sap until little by little we begin to bear the right kind of grapes."

There were "acts" to make in order to give a worthy welcome to Jesus Christ. Philippine set herself grimly to the task of not allowing herself any comforts or treats to nature. She wanted to give all she could. On the great day, she would then be able to ask confidently that her father should come back to the Church. Perhaps he might even before then, and join her at the altar rails.

Some of the older girls, a little jealous of her fervour, teased her.

"I believe you wish we were pagan Romans," said one.

"Or fierce Japanese samurai," put in another.

"Then we could torture you and kill you and you could be a martyr. You'd like that, wouldn't you?"

"Yes," said Philippine in all simplicity.

The nuns did their best to make the day of the First Communion a happy one. There were flowers and a blaze of candles and special hymns and white dresses and friends and relations there in the chapel. But these were only a background scarcely noticed by Philippine. Her father would not be with her in the great moment, but the ache in her heart was caught up into something much bigger. Our Lord in His majestic humility and overwhelming love came into her heart, gave her His Heart to share His desires and longings. He wanted hers in return. All of it. Together they would long for the souls of all men. Martyrdom? Her blood poured out from a mangled body—that was hardly likely in the France of Louis XVI. Her father had told her often that the age of persecution had passed and the reign of reason would do away with intolerance. But a life given wholly to Him, living completely for Him, why, that was here at her very side. Souls could be won by living as well as by dying. He asked. He must give her light to see His Will and strength to follow it. He wanted her in this sanctuary of His Sacred Heart. Like St Francis in the statue, she would hold out her heart in return for His, "Take, O Lord and receive. . ."

"Don't forget to ask Our Lady to preserve all the graces of this day," Mother de Bayanne reminded them.

Of course. This house was hers—the house of Holy Mary on the Heights. She would keep all things safe.

4: Transplantings

NEARLY three years later, M. Duchesne was sitting with his wife at the supper table. Very deliberately he peeled a peach, then moved the candlestand so that he could watch her face.

"My dear," he said, "I think it is time we took Philippine away from Ste Marie's."

She looked up, surprised.

"Why, she hasn't finished her studies and they give such a good report of her. She's good with her needle as well as with her books and it would be a pity to interrupt her training."

"I've no doubt you are right," said her husband. "But there is another side to it. We don't see very much of her—the holidays are so short and she's never quite herself on parlour days—she will be forgetting what family life is."

"Oh, no, not she. She has a very warm, loving heart."

"Quite so. That's what I'm afraid of."

"She's not likely to get sentimental attachments with the nuns, if that's what you mean. I know she appreciates Mother de Bayanne, but then she's holy—there's no silliness there."

"That's my point," said her husband dryly. "I was round at the de la Martinières' the other day. You know Henriette—a proper young chatterbox. She comes out with everything that's in her head. She told me that Philippine spends all her free time in the chapel. Apparently she's been the joke of the school

"She's been the joke of the school because she gets up at the same time as the nuns and makes meditation in the chapel with them."

because she gets up at the same time as the nuns and makes meditation in the chapel with them."

"That exaggeration won't last," Mme Duchesne said.

"But it has," said her husband. "This has been going on ever since she made her First Communion. She gets teased because sometimes in winter she oversleeps and then goes rushing off to the chapel only half dressed so as not to be late and miss her meditation."

He stopped, wiped his knife on a piece of bread, and set back his plate. The supper table spoke of solid comfort, the room in the shadows of the candlelight was the secure background that enwrapped a life that had so much to give of innocent pleasures and mutual love. He looked at the kindly face of his wife before he began again. Would she be first and foremost a Christian or a mother?

"I did not take a girl's chatter as final," he said. "To-day I went up to the convent and saw the Reverend Mother. I asked her outright what Philippine was up to. As I suspected, she wants to be a nun."

Mme Duchesne drew in her breath sharply.

"Oh, no! Not that. She's too young. She doesn't know her mind."

"She'll think she does," said M. Duchesne. "She's not a Duchesne for nothing."

"She must come home," his wife decided, thinking quickly. "She can go on with her studies—my brother will let her join his sons—and then she is old enough to go out with Amélie—there are plenty of concerts this season and dances and healthy young people to go about with. All she wants is distracting—you know, you Duchesnes concentrate on things."

Her husband smiled. Christian principles had not stood up against maternal instincts. He had got his way without a fight.

Philippine came back without comment or protest. Evidently it was what God wanted of her. It did not in the least affect the main issue. Our Lady would look after that.

From her parents' point of view, the move was eminently successful. Year ran into year with a never-flagging round of interests.

"This square turret is just made for a hermitage," said the learned Abbé Raillane, whom M. Périer had engaged to teach his sons. "No other view than sky and rooftops—no other noise than the scratching of your pens. The only pity is that five of you are rather too many for solitude. Mlle Philippine would manage all right, but you boys—"

"That's not fair," said Jean. "I work just as hard at arithmetic as she does—I don't say a word while I'm getting out a problem."

"You know you'd better not," his brother answered. "You'd catch it from father if you wasted time. A banker's son who can't do arithmetic! When it's Latin, I don't know that you're so silent."

"He's all right," Philippine said. "At least when we're translating the Scriptures. Horace will probably kill him."

"*Dulce et decorum est pro patria mori*," Jean quoted the only tag he knew.

"No one wants you to die for France," the Abbé said. "A live dog is better than a dead lion. You've plenty of work to do before your death will have any value for your country."

"Life without end *nobis donet in patria*," retorted the irrepressible Jean. "You'll be sorry for your hard words when I'm a martyr and have laid down my life for that *patria*. Philippine understands my high sentiments."

"M. l'Abbé, have you seen what she's up to here?" cried Antoine, seizing hold of a sheet of paper on which she was working. "It's awfully good, I think."

He held up a pen and ink sketch of a log cabin before which a priest in a cassock stood. Behind rose pine trees and mountain peaks, while on the right a feathered Indian stepped forward with outstretched hand.

"I can't get that hand right," said the artist.

"The trees aren't growing quite properly either," said the Abbé.

"But they're growing," said Jean with admiration. "They're not just sticks."

"Yes," the Abbé agreed. "It's vigorous. I don't think I can teach you anything more, Mlle Philippine. What about trying a portrait of a saint now—St Gertrude or St Clare or St Jane de Chantal?"

"Do you mind if I try St Francis Xavier?" Philippine asked, and set to work.

There were music lessons, too. M. Lamont taught the best families in Grenoble but he confessed himself beaten by Philippine.

"It's strange," he confided to his wife. "She loves music too. But you either have it in you or you don't, I suppose. Now that bright little Mlle Henriette de la Martinière—she's not half so intelligent, but she sings like an angel, and set her down at the harpsichord, and she'll draw the heart out of you. She's got the soft touch and the delicate half-tones that Mlle Philippine lacks. And she gets it without any effort, while the other works like a black at her music."

Philippine came across the priest who had so enthralled them with his tales of Red Indians. The thwarting of years had mellowed him.

"The Kings of this world have checked the spread of the Faith," he told her; "checked, not stopped. I am a Jesuit still though there is no Company of Jesus to belong to. I can save redskin souls as well doing these humdrum duties of a French parish as in blazing trails through the forests of Louisiana. The missionary heart is the essential, don't you agree?"

Philippine shook her head.

"I don't know, Father. I don't see how you can remain still if you've a missionary heart. If you say the word propaganda or Foreign Missions to me, I'm for taking the next coach to Bordeaux or Marseilles."

"You haven't learnt the ways of God yet," he told her. "Well, if I can help you, come to me."

There were plenty of pleasurable amusements, too. The cousins and their young friends went on excursions up the mountain slopes and through the forests. There were drives along the shady avenues leading out from the city to the Château de Vizille which Claude Périer had bought as a country residence. The tennis courts there used to ring with happy laughter as the boys showed off their prowess to the admiring or teasing girls. And in the evenings there would be dances, at home or in the ballrooms of friends. In 1786, there seemed no reason for young persons to be too serious over life. Grenoble was not Paris, but there was a chance of wearing pretty dresses and enjoying oneself.

"That Duchesne girl is looking quite attractive," Mme de Saussure thought to herself as she watched Frédéric partnering her for a minuet. "Not quite as fashionable as she might be, but Frédéric doesn't seem to mind. There's no accounting for his tastes."

The dance over, Frédéric led Philippine to a chair.

"You're very silent, Mlle Philippine," he said. "You dance with as much seriousness and concentration as if you were doing algebra. A louis d'or for your thoughts."

"You wouldn't find them worth that," said Philippine. How surprised he would be if she told him that all the time she had been thinking what happiness it would be to be a nun. "Let me hear yours instead."

"Mine won't interest you," he said. "I'm only a poor poet and can't cut any figure among the military."

He glanced across at Captain de Mauduit, resplendent in his uniform of the dragoons. His match with Amélie Duchesne had been settled satisfactorily. In spite of his brave appearance, thought Frédéric, he was the meekest of men in the company of his imperious wife.

"I'm not so much afraid of you, for all that, as I used to be," he went on. "Perhaps one day I shall insist on your listening to my poems—do you remember when you wouldn't pay attention to Ronsard? I haven't yet plucked up sufficient courage to face your possible laughter, but I have grown in courage."

"We ought to have grown in that," said Philippine. "We're getting on for nineteen."

"A tremendous age," said Frédéric ironically. "We mustn't be chicken-hearted."

They laughed together. Mme de Saussure noted it. She called on Mme Duchesne the next day. The two mothers were in complete agreement. It remained to inform Philippine.

"My dear Philippine," she said, with her husband sitting by, "Charlotte is sixteen now, and already we have had an offer for her hand."

"I'm so glad," said Philippine.

"But we couldn't think of allowing the marriage to take place yet. It would be most unsuitable for her to get married before you."

"I wouldn't mind," said Philippine.

"But we should," her mother answered. "However, there is no need to get alarmed and to think that her wedding must be indefinitely postponed. Mme de Saussure has talked matters over with me, and we are agreed that Frédéric would be an admirable match for you."

"For me?" cried Philippine aghast.

"Certainly," M. Duchesne broke in. "I have every confidence in the wisdom of the choice. There are very sound qualities of head and heart in that young man."

"But I'm not going to get married," said his daughter.

"It need not be for some months," said Mme Duchesne.

"It need not be at all," said Philippine, with force. "I might as well say it now outright. I am going to be a nun."

Mme Duchesne protested. Philippine was adamant. The argument went on.

"Leave her alone," said M. Duchesne at length. "She will come to her senses. It is all a bit sudden for her. Wait. You'll see."

"I've told you my mind," said Philippine, "and now I will live to show you that I mean it."

She took out all her pretty clothes. Charlotte could wear some, the maids could have others. She chose a dark, plain dress and scraped her hair back.

"Why must you look such a frump?" Amélie objected. "Have your rule of day for prayers and good works if you like, but don't advertise the fact by looking so outlandish." But her sister was unmoved.

That year another baby was born. Mélanie Duchesne was a healthy, pretty child, the pride of Mme Duchesne who rejoiced in Philippine's affection for this little sister. Her obstinacy was forgotten for the time.

Winter passed, spring gave renewed sunshine and blue skies. The world was full of life and colour. Only Philippine still wore her dark dress. One day she went through the passage from her house into that of the Périers. She found her aunt alone.

"Aunt," she said, "I want you to help me."

Mme Périer knew her niece.

"Well?"

"It's no good waiting, is it, when God has made His meaning clear?"

"Not the slightest. Sometimes the longer you wait, the more difficult you make it for others."

"I thought so. Well, will you come with me to-day to Ste Marie's? I'll have to enter there some time, and I'd like to see what arrangements Reverend Mother could suggest. I'm not going to be married."

"No, you're not," said her aunt. "*Dieu premier servi*, like Joan of Arc. All right, I'll get ready and come."

They climbed the hill to Ste Marie's in silence. The big door opened and admitted them to the passage that seemed darker than ever this day of sunshine. They waited patiently in the parlour until Reverend Mother de Murinais appeared. The old nun listened to Philippine's story, turning over the possibilities in her mind. Perhaps next year or the year after the opposition at home would have died down. It would be better not to offend a powerful man like M. Duchesne. She would counsel a more conciliatory way of life. A less rigid flaunting of her purpose.

Suddenly Philippine rose to her feet.

"This is the moment," she said, her face flushing with a look of strange delight. "God has put out His Hand and holds me. I must stay now. Aunt, I can't go back with you. I must enter here and now. Don't cry, my dear aunt. You mustn't sorrow when God acts. Mother de Murinais, you will take me, won't you?"

The Reverend Mother had risen too. Caution, common sense, ordinary methods, they just did not matter. Philippine was being held by something beyond her control.

"You shall stay now," said Mother de Murinais.

Mme Périer went down the hill alone.

5: *Tocsin*

THE expected does not always happen. When Mme Périer broke the news to the family, the storm was not let loose. Mme Duchesne wept, but gave no word of blame to her sister-in-law.

"I must recognize God's hand in this," she said at length. "I don't find any fault with what you have done, my dear sister."

M. Duchesne closed his lips tightly.

"We must let her have her way," he said. "I love her too well to make her unhappy. She is mistaken, I think, but it is her own life, not mine, and I will not oppose her peace."

Now that the decisive step had been taken, there was a sense of relief. They would not turn against her in any bitterness. A few days later, they went to visit her.

Philippine's heart stood still when the mistress of novices took her along to the parlour. It was not the familiar one of her schooldays. The nun drew back a curtain at one end, and Philippine found herself looking out on her family through the bars of the grille. They were all there, mother and sisters, down to Mélanie seated on Charlotte's knee, chuckling and patting her face with her chubby hands. Her family. Hers, yet not hers, and yet again, doubly hers. She found no words and for a minute there was silence. Then Mme Duchesne's tears burst forth.

"Oh, Philippine, Philippine," she cried, "come back to us. You are my best of daughters."

"You can't think how we miss you," said Charlotte. "And Father has been so silent these days—he doesn't scold you, but that's all the worse. He wants you so badly."

"You're my oldest now that Amélie is married," said her mother. "You've always been so helpful, so good, so full of common sense. I was looking to you to help me bring up Mélanie."

Philippine felt sick and cold. Her heart went out to them; willingly she would give all she could to them, but how could she not know that God had put out His Hand and taken her? She could not argue. She could only reaffirm her decision. How could they realize in the pain of loss that she would be able to help them more by her prayers and her obedience to God than by anything she could do for them in the world? It was hard even for her to realize it. She only knew by bare faith and an unemotional certainty that it was so.

The minutes of the visit passed, Mme Duchesne's tears flowed on, silently, unreproachfully. Mélanie became fretful and would not look at the unfamiliar big sister. There was nothing left to do now but go. The curtain was drawn across the grille. With her heart torn in two, Philippine ran to the chapel and knelt down before the altar.

"O dearest Lord," she sobbed, "You have helped me to win this fight. I mean to live and die here. St Jane de Chantal, pray for me, your daughter. Sacred Heart of Jesus, take care of my family."

In a few weeks' time, Mother de Murinais gave her the veil of a novice of the Order of the Visitation. There was a great deal to learn, but she put her whole soul into the learning.

"Sister Duchesne's rushing after holiness," Mother Delphine remarked to her superior.

"Literally, in some ways," said the mistress of novices. "If there's any work to be done, she's there before others have begun to think about it."

"Don't let her overdo things," cautioned Reverend Mother de Murinais.

"She has an iron constitution," answered the mistress of novices. "I really think it's hard to get her tired out. She does twice as much as anyone else and then begs for night adoration."

"She'll want more fasts and penances than our rule caters for," said Mother Delphine.

"She'll need them," said the mistress of novices. "She has the Duchesne character. That kind is not driven out but by prayer and fasting!"

Philippine discovered the treasures of the library at Ste Marie's.

"You're living on Rodriguez," one of the sisters teased her at recreation. "He wrote his book on Christian Perfection for Jesuit novices. Don't you wish you were one?"

"If I were a man," answered Philippine, "I wouldn't hesitate. I'd pack up and make my way to Russia and join the remnant of the Society."

"Strange," said another, "with all the prayer you can manage, I should have thought you would have made for Carmel."

"Yes, it's true that I love Carmel very much, but it's only prayer there and I want to work directly for souls as well as to pray for them. That's why I've come here. We do have an opportunity to be apostolic with the children in the school."

"And are there still any lives of Jesuit saints in the library that you haven't read?" asked another nun.

"No," said Philippine, amid general laughter. "But it's all right. I'm reading St Francis Xavier's again. He's my favourite—the one I care most about."

"Why? I should have thought you would have liked Aloysius Gonzaga—he was so young and ardent and so strong in his determination to straighten the twisted iron of his character."

"But he didn't go out to the missions—he never saw India or Japan or the distant shores of China. I get so impatient sometimes to win all those pagans for Our Lord, that I say to St

Francis, 'Great Saint, why don't you call me to follow you?' I
would do so at once."

"Sister Duchesne," said the mistress of novices, "God has
called you to work in France. Don't waste your energies over
unsubstantial dreams."

"Well, there were Jesuit saints who worked in France,"
Philippine countered. "Look at St Francis Regis. Now there's
another saint I love. The way he went about after souls—jour-
neying through the most impossible weather over the wildest
of roads in the midst of the most hostile of heretics and the most
lukewarm of Catholics—giving himself without stint for the
poor and the outcast. Mother Tesseire gave me devotion to
him. I often pray before his relic. He's more easy of imitation."

"But you can't go tramping about Dauphiné like him,
Sister Duchesne. I wonder that you are content to let your
labours be bounded by the two dozen children of our
school—"

"Oh, it's what God wants of me," Philippine answered.
"So it's enough to satisfy all my longings—that, and being able
to pray for the whole world."

Towards the end of her year's noviceship, her sisters, now
Mme de Mauduit and Mme Jouve, came to see her.

"Aren't you bored with your kind of life yet?" Amélie
asked, looking curiously at her through the grille. The habit
certainly suited her; it gave her height and dignity. But that
she herself would not notice.

"Why, are you bored with yours?" asked Philippine. "You
surely find it interesting to work for Captain de Mauduit and
M. Jouve."

"Yes, but then we've so much to talk about."

"What kind of things?" asked Philippine.

"Well, the business connections of my husband give plenty
of subjects for conversation," said Mme Jouve, "and Amélie is
well up in garrison news. Did you know there were quite considerable troops here at the disposition of the Governor?"

"And then there are all the problems Father is facing," said

Amélie. "You don't bother your head about those, I'll be bound, but they're worrying enough, I can tell you."

"I do know they say the quarrel between the King and the *Parlement* is growing," said Philippine. "I'm not quite isolated from France. There doesn't seem much hope of a financial recovery, does there, and changing ministers just makes things worse. It's a pity the King always makes a show of firmness at the wrong moment. But we don't talk about those things—we pray about them instead,"

"Father says that popular opinion is growing every day more and more liberal," said Amélie. "A few months ago, he was really quite pleased with the way in which what he calls the rights of man were being recognized. He thought that it showed that the end of tyranny and privilege was in sight. You know how much he wants to have the same sort of freedom in the government of the country as they've got in the States of America."

"And what does he think now?" asked Philippine as Amélie stopped with a dubious note in her voice.

"He doesn't say very much," she answered. "I thought he would have been pleased last week—we got the news that on 1 May an edict abolishing torture had been issued in Paris—but he hasn't said anything except that the reform of justice is being done in the wrong way. It's all very muddling. I like the King. I can't say as much for the Queen, though she is a lovely woman. But I suppose there must be constitutional reforms. Only I don't know where they're coming from. Some people are demanding a meeting of the States General. Father's against that if they are to be summoned by the King and his ministers only to support their measures. After all, Philippine, you've chosen the better part. You don't have to get a headache trying to sort these things out."

"Yes," said Philippine slowly, "it is the better part."

The conviction grew in the next weeks, as May ended and June came. She was sweeping an upstairs corridor one morning after Mass, with all the vigour that love could put into the task.

"Amélie was right, though she gave the wrong reason," she thought. She opened a window through which the sunlight was flooding. A rush of fresh air entered, cool with the hint of the snow peaks, scented with alpine flowers. The song of birds was suddenly loud. Looking out, she saw the great chain of mountains emerging from the clouds that parted and drifted away. She went on with her sweeping.

"All God's handiwork, clean and untouched by man's sins," she thought. "And this house the house of God—the gate of heaven. I don't wonder that St Mary Magdalen of Pazzi had to kiss her convent walls—how I love Ste Marie's! It is the better part—but Our Lord said, 'I have chosen you, not you Me.' To be perched up here, in the calmness of religious life—what peace, what happiness!"

She stopped abruptly. Through the open window, rising from the town at the foot of the mountain, came, loud and insistent, the clanging of the alarm bell.

6: *Axes*

ALL through the first week of June 1788 there had been unrest in Grenoble. Rumours and counter-rumours had been rife. Travellers by the stage-coaches gave contradictory reports, but, whether they came from the south or the east or the west or the north, all made it clear that the country was perturbed and angry, and no man satisfied with any of the moves that King or ministers or political partisans were making. One thing emerged clearly. The government in Paris was assuming powers beyond any that the provincial *parlements* would tolerate. An assembly of the States General was promised, but in the meantime all other *parlements* were to be prorogued.

"What is Paris that it should suppress us?" the deputies of Dauphiné asked each other.

"Why should we submit to these May Edicts?' the citizens took up the argument.

"This will be the end of our liberties," M. Duchesne told M. Claude Périer. "If we are defrauded of our rights here in our own city, we shall never be able to bring about that reform of our country's constitution that you and I see must come. This will be setting a further seal on privilege and the evils that have grown up round the continuing of a feudal system when the world has changed."

"Grenoble must make a stand," said his brother-in-law. "The rights of the individual man must be saved."

The Governor, the Duke of Clermont-Tonnerre, did his duty as the representative of the King.

"Gentlemen," he told the assembled deputies, "you may no longer meet. The *Parlement* is at an end."

An angry buzz of talk greeted his announcement. The news was passed to those who waited outside the hall. A crowd gathered, growing each moment in size and hostility. The King was taking away the freedom of his subjects. The rights of the city were being filched from them. Grenoble was to be over-ridden by Paris. Liberty was worth fighting for.

A servant emerged from the *Parlement* building.

"Some of the deputies are ordering their coaches and re-turning home," he told the crowd.

A shout arose.

"Stop them, stop them! Ring the alarm bell! Get help to save the freedom of Dauphiné!"

Some bold spirits made a rush for the belfry. The ropes were pulled, the great bells began to swing. Their clanging rang out across the sunlit valley of Grésivaudan. Near-by churches took up the warning notes. Up on the mountains in the little villages, the bells echoed the call. Men seized axes and flintlocks and hastened in bands towards the city—fierce look-ing, hardy mountaineers jostling with the townspeople on their way to the Governor's palace. The market women had hastily packed away their stalls, the shopkeepers closed their shops, the doors of the public buildings were shut. And all the time the alarm bells boomed and clanged.

The temper of the crowd was ugly. Some of the deputies were anxious to get away. M. Mounier and the Périer faction were no doubt right when they spoke of the loss of liberty the King's Edicts entailed, but action was, to say the least of it, in-expedient at the moment. They called for their coaches. Their servants could bring them along to a side entrance and they would show their loyalty to the King in the person of his Governor by not prolonging an unfortunate meeting unneces-sarily. But the crowd saw the manœuvre.

"We'll soon stop that little game," cried a group of men from the mountains. "Here, take out the horses."

Scared, the coachmen undid the traces and led the animals, sweating with fear, through the shouting throng. Then with strong blows of their axes, the mountaineers hacked at the wooden coaches. The chips flew as though they were felling pine trees. Axles smashed, wheels went rolling on to their sides. The crowd laughed and clamoured for more, feeling its strength for the first time.

The Duke of Clermont-Tonnerre knew his duty. He sent word to the garrison for help. An unruly mob must be quelled by show of force.

The beating of the drums of the troops drew yells and cat-calls from the crowd. The sight of armed men roused their fighting spirit. A stone was thrown. A soldier wiped blood from his face. His companions shouldered the angry men and women aside as they marched towards the Governor's palace. But the crowd surged forward with them, striking out, throwing stones and garbage, moving like a mountain torrent in flood. Jostling, hustling, they swarmed through the gateway and into the courtyard. Some bold spirits shinned up drain-pipes and reached the roof. There were loose tiles, and some that only needed a little wrenching to come loose. Down on to the heads of the soldiers they hurled them, while others of their number, discovering a skylight, let themselves down into the house and ran shouting along its corridors. On the ground floor a door yielded before the axe strokes of the assailants. A second body of men broke through and joined those inside, crying out for the Duke. They found him at length in his drawing room, no very impressive figure, undecided whether military duty and honourable loyalty really demanded that he should die like a dog at the hands of the ruffians round about him. Among the mirrors and porcelains and gilded furniture of the room, death was out of place. A small group of frightened servants clustered in the background. A weatherbeaten man brandished an axe over his head. A confused shouting went on. It was hard to gather one's wits together to know what was best to do. The men round him held a paper and pen before him.

"Here, sign this. Pledge yourself to convoke the *Parlement*."

"Sign so that the Edicts will not be put into operation."

Mechanically he took the pen. He stood twisting the quill, still undecided. He glanced up at the axe edge. It gleamed in the sunlight like the prisms of his chandelier. Death while obeying orders—there was the part for a soldier.

"Sign," yelled a fierce-looking tatterdemalion, "or we'll hang you from your own chandelier."

The Duke saw himself twisting lifelessly from those prisms, reflected in the mirrors round the room. An ormulu clock struck with a silver chime. He took the pen, dipped it in the outstretched inkwell, and signed. With a shout of triumph, the crowd withdrew, passing the good news from one to another until all in the street had learnt that the day was won. The men on the roof threw high the last tiles they had loosened. Victory was theirs.

It was dusk before a messenger could reach Ste Marie's. The clanging of the alarm bell all day, the movement of bands of men down the road, the roars of shouting that had come up from the town, had seemed to portend some great disaster. The sun had gone down behind the mountains in a red angry blaze. But now that night had come, and coolness, and silence, their fears were set at rest. There had been bloodshed, but order was restored. The men of Grenoble were satisfied. Their rights had been safeguarded. The morning would bring peace. Yet Philippine as she knelt before the tabernacle alone in the chapel that night could not get the sound of the tocsin out of her mind.

The Duke of Clermont-Tonnerre might yield, but Marshal Vaux was a man of another stamp.

"I know my duty," he said when he came to replace the Duke, and was faced by the Deputies of Dauphiné. "A document signed under duress has no value. Mobs cannot thwart the progress of the law. Under no conditions will I allow the *Parlement* to meet in Grenoble. As you love your city, you will not press the point. I have troops at my command, and any repetition of disturbances will be met with resolute force."

"He is right," M. Duchesne said to his brother-in-law as they discussed the matter with other deputies in the Périer house in the Place St André. "Liberty is not to be won by licence. The violence of undisciplined men is the worst enemy to reform. The will of the crowd in place of the will of the King —that's to substitute one tyranny for another."

"Yet meet we must," said M. Mounier. "The times are ripe for a blow for the rights of the people. We cannot submit to this suppression, and expect to regain our position."

"You are right," M. Duchesne agreed, "but the meeting cannot take place in Grenoble. Marshal Vaux is a man of his word. We cannot risk further troubles and armed force."

"I have it!" cried Claude Périer. "There is the Château de Vizille. It's far enough away to stop the crowds from making their way there and being a nuisance. It's near enough for us deputies to travel there. The tennis-court hall would be the very thing for our assemblies. It's large enough to hold us all with comfort."

Within a week, the *Parlement* of Dauphiné was holding its meetings in the country house of the Périers. Beneath its age-long roofs, men debated with their eyes on the future. The old order of feudal rights was examined and found wanting. The new order when each man should have his own rights was bright on the horizon. They must take the first step towards it. They drew up a document and sent it to the King at Versailles. This was to be no petition to His Majesty from humble subjects: it was a demand that he should convoke the States General without delay. At three o'clock in the morning of 22 July 1788, the Provincial Assembly signed a letter of thanks to Claude Périer for his assistance in the cause of freedom. The work at the Château de Vizille was finished.

M. Duchesne climbed the hill to Ste Marie's alone the following week. He asked to see Reverend Mother de Murinais.

"Madame," he said, "don't misunderstand me. I do not

think as you, but it is through no opposition to my daughter's choice that I am here to-day. She will soon have completed her year's noviceship, isn't that so?"

"Yes," said Reverend Mother de Murinais. "Profession follows—that means she will take vows binding her to the convent and our life."

"Then formally I forbid that step to be taken. I am too well aware of the forces at work in France. To-day they are fighting the King, to-morrow it will be the Church that is attacked. And when the Church is attacked, it is the religious orders that are in the front line. Philippine is only nineteen. She does not realize the danger. I don't ask that she should leave Ste Marie's. I only refuse my consent to her final profession until she is twenty-five. You, Madame, will see the wisdom of this. My daughter will be only too ready to take vows that will seem to her like a prelude to martyrdom. May I count on your support in a decision that is, to say the least of it, prudent?"

Reverend Mother de Murinais was silent for a minute. Of course it was a wise move. But beyond the human wisdom she glimpsed something still more wise. God was a gardener who understood His plants. How Philippine would hate waiting! Martyrdom would be easy in comparison.

"Certainly you may count on me, M. Duchesne," she said.

7: Gathering Storm Clouds

To Philippine the decision was like a midnight blackness at midday. She had been living for months for the moment when, her vows pronounced in the presence of the whole court of heaven, she could say, "Lord, I am all Yours. Yours for time and Yours for eternity." Every minute of the day had been bright with the sunshine of that thought. It was that that had sent her about the household tasks with springing step; it was that that had sent her hurrying like St Aloysius, to the chapel. The anticipation had made joy thrill through her in the night watches before the Blessed Sacrament. And now it was as if He Himself had repulsed her. If it had been her father alone, she would have fought, but Reverend Mother spoke, and hers was the voice of authority, the delegated authority of God Himself. Obedience, Holy Obedience, held her submissive in will, if not in feelings.

"I can see no light in the future," she told herself, and indeed the darkness was complete. "This is the hardest trial that God could have sent me."

Mother Delphine, growing old now and needing a stick, laughed at her distress.

"You might be a Dutchman from the way you speak," she said. "And you a native of Dauphiné!"

"What has that to do with it?" asked Philippine.

"Why, if you had been brought up in a country of wide,

47

flat spaces and long views, I'd excuse your being upset because
the way doesn't stretch clearly before you. But when you've
lived among mountains, you should know that the path doesn't
disappear in actuality when a mist comes down. It'll be there if
you wait where you are until the mist drifts away. You've been
thinking, too, that you've climbed the mountain of God when
you've reached your profession day—and yet you know how
sometimes quite a little summit can hide the much steeper
slopes beyond. You've got to the top now, and you find that it
isn't the top. Well, can't you wait for the guide to show you
the way?"

"Wait," said Philippine. "It's very hard to wait six years.
And I shall be twenty-five when I have waited. I shall be getting
old."

"You won't be old when you're twice twenty-five," said
Mother Delphine. "And if you have to wait, can't you trust
Our Lord's Sacred Heart? He knows."

She told her grief to a wise priest who visited the convent.
Surely a man would see a way out, would not be content to
waste years of life in this way. She did not get the answer she
expected.

"Let us adore the will of God," he said. "He knows what
He is doing, and He knows the future result of what He per-
mits now. You will understand all this hereafter."

She did not understand it now, but if it was God's will, she
was not going to accept it sulkily. If she was to be a novice still,
then she would be as good a novice as she had always tried to
be. She took up her work again with vigour.

Perhaps because her own future depended on it, perhaps because her family was so intimately concerned, she found herself thinking much about the progress of events in France. In
the early months of 1789, her mother, visiting her in the parlour, told her that the election of the States General was taking
place.

"Your father is doubtful about it all," she said. "There are
some good men among the members—Mirabeau, Mounier

from here, some clergy who have heads on their shoulders—but too many half-educated representatives, wise in their own conceits and not experienced in political matters. He says that such men are easily moved by anyone who is eloquent. There are lawyers among them but they'll not be numerous enough to give weight in the sifting of arguments."

Later in the year, it was Mme Jouve who gave Philippine her husband's opinion.

"He thinks that it is a good thing that the States General are demanding a new constitution—something on the lines of the English or American one. All the representatives are going with lists of grievances—there won't be any wrong left unmentioned. He thinks that's a good thing—I say, no. If you invite people to grumble, they'll find all sorts of grouses that they wouldn't have thought about, and they'll exaggerate their sufferings by adding everyone else's together. He says they'll put forward a good programme of reform, and in conjunction with the King and his minister, the new constitution will be drawn up. But I say the King isn't interested enough, and as for Necker—he's no statesman, and one of Uncle Périer's bank clerks would be about as fit to tackle the human situation."

In the third week of July, it was M. Duchesne himself who came to give the news.

"The Bastille has fallen. People are saying that it is a symbol —a symbol all can read—of the downfall of absolutism. It may well be. But what does it portend for the future?"

"I thought you would have rejoiced, Father."

"How can I? If absolutism has been defeated, it has been by the wrong means. Mistake after mistake has been made. It was a mistake for the States General to meet at Versailles—it was too near to Paris and Paris is seething with a hungry rabble of unemployed. It was foolish to use the term National Assembly and to pass measures quite illegally as though it really was the properly reconstituted National Assembly. That has thrown them more and more into the necessity of playing down to the people. It is foolish now to withdraw the troops from Paris—

it's leaving the moderate, reasonable parties at the mercy of the wilder elements. And Paris will give the lead to other parts of the country. There are too many hungry men and women in France—they'll take desperate measures once the framework of law and order begins to break."

The much needed harvests that year were ripening well.

"At least there will be that much help to hand," thought Philippine, as she looked down on the valley of Grésivaudan, lying under the sunlight at the foot of the mountains. But even as she looked, over the white peaks of the distant range, a wisp of grey cloud floated down. The sky behind darkened till the mountains stood out grim and purple, and the grey cloud surged over them curling and stretching out like smoke from a furnace. The air grew heavy and the brightness left the day. Then forked lightning cut across the sky, and in a minute the storm had burst. Hail of unprecedented size and violence poured down. The wind swept over the fields beating down the crops and tearing up trees. When the storms had passed, farmers all over France were looking with despair at ruined harvests, and the clamour for food grew louder. At Ste Marie's, they heard tell of bands of men, who, folk said, were in the pay of the nobility, brigands who prowled about the country destroying what crops were left, in order to starve the people into submission. Peasants had begun to arm themselves. In the towns the citizens had attacked and taken their bastilles. The châteaux of the nobles were being seized and burnt. Men who loved France and wished to prevent the spread of anarchy were seeking safety and help abroad. There was anger at rumours of heartless banquets in Versailles, while the people of Paris lacked food. The Assembly was not moving fast enough for the proletariat. The Assembly had abolished feudal rights. The Assembly had confiscated the property of the Church. The King was refusing to sanction their decrees. Necker was reporting the bankruptcy of the country. Ten thousand women clamouring for bread had marched to Versailles. The King, with the Queen, had been forced to go to Paris and live in the Tuileries. By the year's end, he was virtually a prisoner. It was difficult to sift truth from untruth in the rumours, but, plain for all to see, the dark clouds of a storm that had not yet burst in all its violence had gathered.

Seventeen hundred and ninety brought no alleviation. Life in a convent might continue within its appointed lines, but in the country all accepted lines were being rubbed out. The Assembly decreed the suppression of religious orders, but the machinery to accomplish this was not yet forthcoming. A year of plots and counter-plots, of risings and massacres, of unrest and mutiny in the army, of complete financial breakdown, of the springing up of more and more Jacobin societies, of growing strength in the National Guard, and at its end, the power in the country was ready for Robespierre and for Marat. They voiced the will of the people, they would be able, when the time came, to put that will into effect.

Representatives of the Assembly called on Reverend Mother de Murinais in the first week of the new year, 1791. They presented their credentials. They showed her a copy of the decrees of the previous year.

"Am I to understand from this that you are taking over all Church property?" she asked.

"That is so," one man answered her, a little discountenanced by her calm reading of his document. "But you will see that it is all in legal form. The law of last February has deprived your monastic vows of all legal force. You, too, Madame, are a citizen of France and need be bound to no foreign power. There is every reason to suppose that when you have taken off your religious dress, you will be allowed to carry on here—Grenoble will still need a school."

He felt uncomfortable as she smiled and kept silence. She was an old woman; perhaps she had not taken in the full meaning of his visit.

"Will you give me time to think this over?" she said at last.

"You must tell the rest of your community," he said. "I have the list of them here. Forty-five nuns in all."

"That is right," said the Reverend Mother. "Yes, I will tell them. And you will come again for the answer. When?"

The deputation consulted among themselves.

"We can give you until 14 January," said their spokesman. "You understand. There are now no longer any religious orders. Ste Marie must be used for secular purposes."

Reverend Mother de Murinais went to the chapel, as they left. Her community were all there saying office.

"I was glad when they said unto me, We will go into the house of the Lord," chanted one choir.

"Our feet shall stand in thy gates, O Jerusalem," the second choir responded.

The Reverend Mother sighed inwardly. She would have to tell them that the house of the Lord was no longer theirs. They would have to pray long and earnestly before they made their decision. It must be their decision, not hers. But she was their mother. Her example and her prayer must be their help. There was still a week's grace before them.

On 14 January at midday the deputation climbed the hill again. It was a bitter, gusty day, and the snow like dry sand cut against their faces. Reverend Mother de Murinais was waiting for them. She handed them a roll of paper without a word.

"Your title deeds?" asked the leader, as he unrolled the scroll. She smiled.

"Yes," she answered.

Another man looked over his shoulder and cried angrily, "It's no such thing. It's a protest—see, signed by every man-jack of them—"

"Forty-five nuns in all," said Reverend Mother de Murinais quietly. "You will see there that we state that we are religious until death. The solemn vows we have taken, the promises we have made to Almighty God, those are our title deeds, those give us the right to live and die nuns of the Visitation. You may take Ste Marie's from us, you may pass any law you like to deprive us of liberty or life, but you cannot unmake us. We are religious by a higher law than that of the National Assembly."

The men murmured with surprise at her boldness.

"You know the consequences of this?" they asked.

"Perfectly," said Reverend Mother de Murinais.

"You must make preparations for departure at once," said their leader. "We shall go now, but you'll be hearing from us very soon."

Angrily they trooped out. Reverend Mother de Murinais felt suddenly very old. There was so much to do. True, Mother de Bayanne, now in a convent in Italy, was ready to welcome many of her daughters, true she could place others in houses outside France or temporarily with friends, but she was leaving the house that she had lived in since she entered as a young girl of seventeen. After more than fifty years, it was hard to think of going elsewhere. The nuns were fervent now. How would the future find them when the moments of heroism had passed? She felt too tired to think of the coming months, perhaps of the coming years. God must look after His own. It was beyond her.

The dark of the evening had fallen when M. Duchesne called at the convent.

"I must see my daughter," he said. "There are preparations being made in the town for the evacuation of Ste Marie's. I am ready to take her away with me. I have a carriage lower down waiting."

Philippine protested. When others were going into exile, it was hard to be sheltered.

"I could go to Italy, to Mother de Bayanne," she pleaded. Her father looked at her tenderly. It was her great heart that spoke, but her plan was not wise.

"No, Philippine," he answered. "The times are too dangerous. This trouble in France may well break out in other countries. Or there may be war. No. Get your things together and come. I have your Reverend Mother's consent."

She went off to her cell. There were few things to put together. A prayer book, an office book. She had kept nothing that was not strictly necessary, practising that vow of poverty she had not been permitted to make. She wept as she took her leave of the other nuns, and of Reverend Mother de Murinais. She turned into the chapel. The statue of Our Lord pointed to His Sacred Heart. She longed to take hers and hold it out like St Francis and show Him the wound in it that bled now at the thought of leaving Him. He was in the tabernacle. Perhaps in a few days the tabernacle would be empty. An empty chapel, desolate and useless, perhaps for ever.

"O Sion," she cried as she took a backward look through the open door, "shall I never see thee again? O Lord, wilt Thou not break the bonds that detain me amongst the children of Kedar?"

But there was no answer to her heart. At the door her father put round her shoulders a heavy travelling cloak of his that he had brought, and pulled the hood over her head and veil. Outside against the lamp of the doorway she could see the gusts of snow rising from the street. It was dark as her father guided her down through the archway on to the cobbled way that led to the road. It was dark as the carriage drove through the city and brought them to the Place St André. But there was light inside and her mother there to welcome her.

"I've put you in your old room right upstairs," she whispered. "You'll be alone there. I've put a dress of mine there for you. Don't come down to-night if you don't want to."

In her bedroom Philippine's tears flowed deep and noiselessly as she took off her habit and folded her veil and shut them into a drawer. Her mother had chosen a dark simple gown and laid it on the bed. That was the dress she must wear in the morning.

8: Foes Without

MÉLANIE was enchanted. King and commoners might quarrel, sceptre and crown topple down, but chasing butterflies and gathering forget-me-nots at the edge of a stream were far more important and the move from Grenoble to Granne in the Drôme one of unmixed delight. There were the preparations first of all, days of standing by when cases and trunks were being filled with all sorts of useful things taken from chests and cupboards she had never explored before. It was fun to go down to the courtyard in the early morning and watch the servants loading them on to a farm-cart, with its driver flicking his whip and the two horses stamping impatiently until they were off into the deserted street. She had been a little frightened the last evening when she had pushed open the door of the big drawing-room and had found all the furniture shrouded with covers. In the faint light that came through the cracks in the closed shutters, the familiar chairs and tables looked ghostly and strange, and she had stood there with an empty feeling inside that made her want to cry, but Philippine had come behind her and had picked her up in her arms and carried her off to bed. They had started off themselves very early the next morning—she with her mother and Philippine and Cousin Marie Tranchant in one carriage, while her father and the others came on later. Then there was the exciting two-days' journey through the mountains—a kind of prolonged picnic with the fun of staying the night in an old inn where the carriage horses were put in the same shed as the cows and the milk she drank came straight from the pail.

"Will I have a cow when we get to Granne?" she asked.

"There'll be lots of cows and some goats and hens and chickens," Philippine told her. "We'll be proper farmers, you see."

At last the road brought them within sight of a hill.

"What's that on top?" Mélanie asked again.

"That's an old ruined castle," her sister answered, while her cousin sighed, and added, "That's typical, Philippine. A sign of the times. The end of feudalism."

But the Duchesne country house was in good repair, and they were soon settled in and life took on a different shape from the old city life in Grenoble. Country life was full of all sorts of things to do, and in the freshness of early summer it was all great fun. Of course there were times when Mélanie knew she must not interrupt Philippine and Cousin Marie. They got up each morning at five, and said long prayers together.

"Why?" asked Mélanie one day.

"Well, you see, Cousin Marie and I are really still nuns, and we're doing what nuns do," Philippine explained.

"Oh, Philippine," Marie remonstrated, "don't tell her things like that. She's only just five and she won't know what she ought not to say if she's ever questioned."

"Mélanie knows how to keep a secret, don't you, Mélanie?" said Philippine. "And anyhow, suppose we were taken to prison, it would be a glorious thing, wouldn't it, to suffer for our faith!"

There was another secret that Mélanie knew she must not talk about. There were two men living at Granne. Philippine called them "Father", and told Mélanie that they belonged to a kind of army with a man named St Ignatius at their head and they went out fighting devils. Mélanie used to look for their swords and when they disappeared one day and did not come back, she wanted to know if they had gone to buy some. Cousin Marie laughed and said they would get them in a shop called

Russia. Cousin Marie was nice, but not so nice as Philippine. Mélanie liked Wednesdays because they were both so happy that day.

She soon found the reason.

"Would I be nice if I didn't have any breakfast?" she asked her mother.

"I don't think so," said Mme Duchesne. "Little girls must eat and do as they're told."

"Don't big girls have to?" Mélanie persisted.

"Yes," Mme Duchesne answered. "But you see, Philippine and Cousin Marie have been told to fast on Wednesday."

"Who told them?"

"It's their rule," Mme Duchesne explained. "And if people keep their rule, they are happy."

"Can't I have a rule?" asked Mélanie.

"Perhaps, when you are older."

Mélanie registered a resolve to have the same one as Philippine and Marie. She almost felt she had it when she went for walks down to the chapel. It was in the village, and the path to it lay across fields and through the woods. When she had helped Philippine in the kitchen or scullery, and had said her daily lessons, she would go with her there. It was a dark little place, with steps leading down into it. When the door opened, it smelt damp like a crypt, but Philippine would kneel straight up before the tabernacle and Mélanie would imitate her. If her eyes wandered to the picture of St Francis Xavier with St Francis Regis, Philippine would tell her how to pray to them, and sometimes would whisper a story about them. Then Mélanie would see the whole church crowded with souls, white and black and brown and yellow, for the story always told of the way these two saints went gathering souls for God and bringing them into the Church. Then they would say the Litany of the Saints together and end with the prayer that St Francis Xavier made for infidels. Mélanie did not understand that one but it meant that the time in the church was over and they would be going out again into the sunlight and would per-

E

haps see the priest. He was a bit like someone in a fairy-tale—
appearing and disappearing. One day in the autumn when the
leaves were whirling down from the trees, they went to the
church and found the door locked. They looked through the
window. There was no flicker of light in the sanctuary lamp.
The place was empty.

"Our Lord has gone," Philippine told Mélanie, with tears
in her eyes. "You must pray for Father Ravenas."

"Why?" said Mélanie.

"Because this means there are wicked men chasing him and
it won't be safe for him to come back here again," Philippine
said.

There was no Mass for them now. Through the winter news
came of more and more acts of terrorism, of vacillating conduct from the King, and, with the spring of 1792, of foreign
armies massing on the frontiers. Mélanie began to be more
aware of the moods of seriousness that came upon her father
and mother, and her older sisters and cousin. Philippine was
very careful to teach her her catechism and to see that she said
her prayers. There were prayers for all sorts of people, and always prayers for priests.

"There can't be any Mass without them," Philippine explained. "And no Holy Communion. So pray for them,
Mélanie, pray for them."

M. Duchesne found life in the little backwater of Granne
peaceful, a quiet place in a noisy world. He began to feel, in the
midst of legal business that took him away from time to time,
that his country estate was a point of sanity and stability, that
he could best serve France at the moment by carrying on the
work of planting and reaping and rearing stock, the agelong,
unchanging work of the soil.

"We must cultivate our garden," he thought ruefully.
"There are weeds in the political garden, but here at least I can
carry on the labour of the land."

It was a stroke of luck that, earlier in the year, he had been
approached by Pondebard when he was wanting to build a new

mill at Granne. The man was efficient—more than efficient.
He could be relied on utterly. He had put through the business
of superintending the building so well, that M. Duchesne had
had no hesitation in asking him to remain as steward. The men
liked him and he carried on trustworthily in the absence of his
master. He might even in the future be of further use if things
went from bad to worse. It was lucky that Granne lay away
from the main thoroughfares of France. M. Duchesne had been
in Lyons in the second week of July when the battalion of the
men from Marseilles marched through. The whole city had
lined the roads to see them pass, upright, well-born young men
for the most part, their eyes burning with enthusiasm, well
equipped with cannon and wagons, making the air resound
with their warlike song. It was a tune that got into the blood,
that set the feet marching, that kindled the heart with love of
country and hatred of tyranny. "To arms, citizens!" The words
went echoing in the mind long after the men had passed away.
It would echo all along the road that led from the great port of
the south to the great city of the north. It would fire men. It
would set the torch to the final conflagration. M. Duchesne
sighed and let his glance wander round the scene before him.
His fields were growing yellow with wheat; the vines on the
hillside were ready for the vintage. On the green slopes of the
hill beside the ruined castle he saw Philippine with Mélanie.
Then he turned to the man who was approaching from the
farm buildings. It was Pondebard.

"May I speak to you?" he asked as M. Duchesne recognized
him. "I think the time has come when I should be more open
with you. I have striven to serve you well—"

"That is so," said M. Duchesne. "I have every reason to
thank you."

"You have never asked for information about my previous
work," said Pondebard. "It is better that I should now be frank
and tell you."

"As you please," said M. Duchesne. "As a lawyer, I can
read character and I am ready to trust you."

"Thank you," answered Pondebard, "and I too by my trade have been trained to read character, and therefore trust you. though I know that you will not welcome what I say."

"What was your work before you came here?" asked M. Duchesne.

"I was a priest," said Pondebard, and waited.

"M. l'Abbé," said M. Duchesne, "I am pleased to make your acquaintance." He smiled, then added, "But not nearly so pleased as my wife will be—or my daughter Philippine."

The Abbé Pondebard looked at him in surprise. M. Duchesne went on.

"May I ask you to continue with us? Your secret is safe with me. I am not one who holds with priests, as you have discovered, no doubt, but I would be the last to hand you over to the justice of the people. And as for my family, they are hungering for the ministrations of religion. Anything you can do for them, you may. All I ask is that you should be discreet."

The Abbé smiled now.

"A man who has escaped the guillotine by a hair of his head has learnt a lesson of discretion," he said.

So when the September Massacres made the streets of Paris run with blood, when Danton, Marat, and Robespierre let loose the wildest passions of the mob, when in January 1793 the bleeding head of Louis XVI was lifted high above the scaffold and men shouted, "Long live the Republic", at Granne in the stillness of midnight hours, the Holy Sacrifice was offered, and God entered into the hearts of a small band of faithful, loving women, and the soul of Christian France lived on.

Those were days of anguish and sorrow. The Abbé Pondebard laid deep in the minds of the Duchesne children the truths of their faith. Those stood firm no matter what men might do. The winter months seemed endless, cold and bleak. Mme Duchesne fell ill. It was sweet that Philippine was there to nurse her. She had given her daughter to God, and God had given her back again. Her other children were dear to her, but none knew quite so well how to comfort her. Philippine gave her strength and courage to bear her illness. And maybe it was the prayers of Philippine that had brought a priest to their house to minister to her in her spiritual need. The spring would come at last, spring in the woods and mountains with fresh flowers and warm sun; spring, too, in France with fresh rule and peaceful days.

But when spring came, there was civil war in La Vendée, Revolutionary Committees in every commune of France for the arrest of suspected citizens, Fouquier-Tinville was Procurator General, and Mélanie was hiding her tears in Philippine's arms as they knelt by the bedside of their dead mother.

9: *And Foes Within*

PIERRE François Duchesne felt his loneliness after the death of his wife. An austere strand in his character had always made it difficult for him to show his affections. His keen mind wanted the love of another mind that could understand and share his thoughts. In Philippine he recognized such a one, but that very likeness was a barrier. They must both be utterly sincere, admitting no compromise in what they saw as the truth. She did not hold his enlightened views: he could not admit the claims of the Church. They who had so much in common must love each other across an impassable gulf. Perhaps in time she would move forward from her unphilosophical position. He would have to wait, though his heart ached to draw closer to the one of his children who, he knew, most wished to be all she could to him. Meanwhile, there was this letter from his mother.

"Philippine," he said, "your grandmother has written. She seems to have news of several of our friends—and not to approve of their goings on. General de Saussure, she says, has gone to join the royalist party that is entrenching itself in Toulon. Mme de Saussure and Frédéric are in England with other émigrés. She calls it treachery to France to have anything to do with the English. The de la Martinières are in Switzerland. Your grandmother thinks that a stupid step since she foretells the spread of revolutionary ideas to the Swiss cantons."

"Poor Grandmama," said Philippine with a smile. "She's always better in her judgements than anyone else. If they're all wrong, what does she propose doing herself?"

"Staying where she is at Romans," said M. Duchesne. "It would take more than a revolution to move her. But that's the point of the letter. She thinks that one of her granddaughters should come to live with her, to help her run the house. She says that now you are no longer needed to nurse your mother, you could go."

"But what about Mélanie?" asked Philippine.

"She has answered that objection," said her father. "Mélanie is six now; she thinks that you might well be a dangerous influence to her—that you have done your part in her upbringing and that your other sisters are old enough to take the further responsibility now. I think you should go. It's your duty at this moment, and it'll certainly be a good substitute for conventual penance."

Philippine got ready her few necessary belongings and went off. She felt glad of this opportunity to do a hard thing in the interests of charity. She laid her plans as the carriage brought her nearer and nearer to her grandmother's estate on the outskirts of Romans. She would be as gentle as a daughter to the old lady, relieving her of any business with her tenants, leaving her free to pray or read or sew or just to sit and think the long quiet thoughts that satisfy the memories of the very old. Her own twenty-four years were quite strong enough to shoulder all the work and all the troubles that would befall her as the acting head of the household. It would be good to be able to offer this labour of loving charity to God. The carriage pulled up in front of the house at last and she went up the steps and rang at the door. She was kept waiting, but at length it was opened by a maidservant, big, red-cheeked, and placid. Their eyes met, they appraised each other, and both smiled.

"You'll be Mlle Philippine," said the woman. "I'm Rose. Your grandmother is expecting you."

She stopped, and listened. A voice called from a room along the corridor.

"All right," Rose called back. "I'm bringing her at once."

She put her finger on her lips, and led the way. She pushed open the heavy door and Philippine went in. There were shutters half over the windows and the last rays of the sun were making patterns on the well-polished floor. Her grandmother was sitting bolt upright in a carved oak chair, her bony hands grasping the two arms.

"Come in," she said, "and shut the door. Can't you feel the draught you're making there, standing with it open? And I wish to goodness you'd remember to open the shutters, Rose."

"You asked for them to be shut, ma'am," said Rose, obediently going to them.

"Can't you use your common sense?" said Mme Duchesne, ignoring her granddaughter. "Half an hour ago there was too much sun—it's quite a different matter now. You can leave us, Rose. Don't forget to make my gruel thicker for supper to-night."

Philippine hesitated. She would have liked to go forward and kiss her grandmother, but the moment seemed to have passed.

"You're late," the old lady remarked accusingly. "I've been expecting you the whole afternoon."

"The horses found the drive a hot one," Philippine began.

"Don't make excuses," Mme Duchesne interrupted. "Well now you are here, you'd better settle in as soon as possible. Is that all the luggage you've brought with you?" she asked, glancing down at the bag Philippine had placed on the floor.

"Yes, Grandmama," said Philippine.

"You're too old to call me by that child's title," said Mme Duchesne.

"Yes, Grandmother," Philippine agreed.

"Haven't you anything more to say for yourself than 'Yes, Grandmother'?" Mme Duchesne went on. "I suppose few words are part of your silly ideas about still being a nun. Haven't you brought any pretty dresses with you? I don't want to be depressed more than I need, so for goodness sake try to be a bit lively. And don't go introducing any of these new-fangled revolutionary notions. There's your sister Amélie calling herself Citoyenne Mauduit. Citoyenne! I'll not be called Citoyenne Duchesne."

"It's safer these days," began Philippine, but her grand-mother cut in.

"Safer! I'd like to meet the man who dared to call me that! I don't stand any nonsense with my tenants here, I can assure you. Citoyenne! What next! Why, I'd have Rose ordering me about if I allowed that sort of terminology."

Philippine escaped at last. Outside the door, Rose was wait-ing patiently. She smiled again and led Philippine in silence to her room.

"You'll join Madame at supper," she said. "At seven-thirty. I'll see that they give you a good meal. Madame would not per-mit it any earlier. But you will understand?"

"Oh, yes," said Philippine. She was hungry and thirsty after her long journey, but this was a penance she could well put up with. It was not hard to fast.

At seven-thirty she went down to her grandmother. The old lady had taken the head of the table which was set as though for a royal guest. Another maid waited on them, offering the dishes to a running commentary of rebuke and criticism. Mme Duchesne took nothing and watched her granddaughter keenly.

"You're not eating enough to keep a fly alive," she said. "I shall have you breaking down and having to be nursed."

"I never want a great deal," said Philippine.

"Then you should," said the old lady. "A girl your age ought to have a healthy appetite. I don't mean she should over-eat. That's what Lucille here does. I shall be bankrupt if I have to have many more like her."

Lucille flushed angrily and bit her lip.

"Now don't show your temper like that," remarked Mme Duchesne. "You ought to have learnt self-control."

Lucille slapped down the dish she was handing.

"Well, then, I haven't, so there," she cried. "And I'm about tired of all your carping, Madame. So I'll just be off home again and you can find someone else to bully."

She flounced out, slamming the door. Philippine rose in distress.

"Let her alone," ordered her grandmother. She looked a little red, but not put out. "I knew she wasn't the sort to take training. I knew it all along. Rose thought she could recommend her, but I was right, you see. Ring the bell. Rose will come."

Rose appeared with a basin of gruel. Mme Duchesne took it.

"It's much too thick," she said. "Can't you manage to strike the happy mean? And I shall burn my throat with it. Put it down to cool."

Rose set it beside her mistress and went quietly on with the interrupted work of serving Philippine. She listened while she was directed to ask the younger sister of the cook to come into service the next day. Philippine thought it sounded more like a royal command than a request.

"You're lucky to have someone to turn to," she remarked by way of making conversation.

"They are lucky to have someone to employ them," retorted her grandmother. "This gruel is too cold now. Why didn't you remind me to take it?"

"I didn't like to interrupt you when you were directing Rose," said Philippine.

"They haven't taught you much sense in your convent," her grandmother said tartly, but Rose had gone out with the basin, and when she returned, the gruel was to the old lady's liking. When she had finished, she rose.

"Give me your arm," she said. "I retire now. Rose locks up the house. I don't trust the other servants. You will retire too. I can't have you getting up early in the morning. Your room is just over mine and I don't want to be disturbed before seven. I shall be seeing the men about business at nine. I shall expect you to be ready to be there."

They went along the corridor. Half way up the stairs, Mme Duchesne withdrew her arm.

"You're about as much help as a babe in arms," she said. "Where's Rose?"

"I'm doing my best," said Philippine sharply.

"Don't answer back," said her grandmother, and as Rose appeared, went off without saying good night.

"Heavens," thought Philippine in her own room. "This is going to be hard. I've lost my temper once, and I've not been here more than four hours."

At nine the next day it was not difficult to locate her grandmother. Her imperious voice could be heard scolding the bailiff. Philippine waited in the hopes that the scolding would soon come to an end, but at length went into the room in the hopes that her arrival might end it. She was wrong. Her grandmother's sarcasm was directed at her. It was a pity that she had not been taught the value of time, and an understanding of punctuality. Philippine managed to remain silent, though words rose easily to her lips and her grandmother then proceeded with the man. That over, she told Philippine to admit the next person.

"Ah, Pauline," she said as an elderly woman appeared. "I wanted to tell you that I shall be having repairs done to your roof this week. So you had better spend the next few days with your sister-in-law."

The woman hesitated.

"Could you not wait a bit?" she asked. "I'm sorry to put my sister-in-law out by going to her just now. Next month it would be easy, but this week—"

"So I am to be put out instead?" asked the old lady fiercely. "Upon my word, it's a strange state of affairs when I must wait upon your convenience. In that case, the repairs had better be cancelled."

The woman opened her mouth, then shut it again.

"Can't you do it later?" Philippine ventured to ask.

"Don't interfere with what you don't understand," her grandmother said.

The woman went out, but as she passed, she whispered to Philippine, "I'll be seeing Rose about this."

It did not take Philippine long to discover that "seeing Rose" was the one refuge for all her grandmother's employees and neighbours. She found herself seeing Rose whenever the old lady became too cantankerous for her. Nothing seemed to put Rose out. A galley slave could not have had a worse time, yet she bore all the abuse of her mistress patiently.

"How do you manage it?" Philippine asked. "You are a perfect lamb for gentleness. I would have given my grandmother a piece of my mind long ago."

"Poor old dear," said Rose placidly, the slow smile lighting up her face. "It hurts you to see her in that state. She can't help being a tartar. She's too old to be able to alter it now. You've just got to put up with her and bear her temper. She can't be cured, so why get angry with her?"

"That's good of you to think like that, Rose," said Philippine. "I hope you will always feel towards her with so much charity. No one else would stand what you put up with. I hope you will not desert her."

Alone, she thought to herself: "The same blood runs in my veins as in my grandmother's. I am of the same race. I feel within myself already those same imperious desires to have everything my way. I am tempted to think myself right and to criticize others adversely. As I grow older, will these same impetuous dispositions become stronger and stronger, until I am the bane and torment of my family? I must learn not to expect too much from my neighbours. In this life perfection cannot be found. I shall always have to put up with the defects of others as they put up with mine. If I do not check my pride and wilfulness now, I shall become an unloving and unloved old woman."

She sighed. Where was the model for her to follow? If she was back in Ste Marie d'en Haut, the question would be easily answered. "Jesus, meek and humble of Heart, make my heart like unto Thine." That was what she needed. Could she stay here when every moment she was roused to anger by the old lady? Was it deserting the post to which she had been appointed if she went? Where were her dreams of gentle, loving charity? She had failed in her task. At least she had learnt the weakness of her own character. Well, she must try to do better, to meet fault-finding with the soft answer that turneth aside wrath. She would do better.

At supper that night, her grandmother looked across at her.

"Philippine," she said, "you will pack up your things to-night. I have ordered the carriage for you to-morrow. I can't think why your father sent you here. You are absolutely no help to me, and you have a rude manner of answering back that you should have corrected years ago. You show far too much independence of spirit for a girl your age. Be ready to start at ten."

In the carriage the next morning Philippine felt like a defeated general. They were driving back on the road to Granne. She would have to admit that she had not accomplished the work she had set out to do. Suddenly she leant forward to the driver.

"Take me to St Marcellin," she said, "not to Granne."

10: *The Prison on the Hill*

To Philippine, St Marcellin was a turning point. It was as if God had set her there in the silence and solitude of a retreat to see the world more clearly as He saw it. God—the one great fact of life—God loving the world—each individual in it—herself—Marie Antoinette—Robespierre—men able to find their happiness only in that love—men unmindful of it—bitter—hating God and hating each other—God showing His love in the human Heart of His Son—the urgent cry of that Heart, "Feed My lambs, feed My sheep"—tears in the eyes of the God-Man for men like sheep without a shepherd—hands of the God-Man outstretched—"Pray the Lord of the harvest for labourers": these were the realities.

There were generous souls labouring even now when all looked lost, men, and women too, suffering openly for Him in prison or on the scaffold—not sheltering among the hills and woods of Granne. It was with them that she desired to be, spending and being spent in the danger zone. Then like a dagger through her heart came the thought of her father. How she loved him, how she longed to be with him, surrounding him with the warmth of little attentions that only a loving knowledge could give, cheering him when moods of loneliness and disappointment came upon him. Cheering him with what? Not with the only things that could give consolation since, for him, God speaking through the person of Jesus Christ His Son was no more than a tinkling cymbal. She had not the power to make him truly peaceful and happy. God's grace alone could do that. But by devoting herself entirely to God, who ruled over every event and swayed the hearts of men, she could do more for her father than by her presence. The sweetness of her ardent longings to serve God to the full drained away, and bitterness at the thought of the pain she must give filled her. She begged God to let all the suffering of the separation fall upon her alone, but as she prayed, she knew that he must suffer too, that, not understanding, he would resent her leaving him. This would be her anguish, to go forward seeing things in the light of eternity while others saw them in the light of time.

When her decision had been made, Philippine could not bear delay. The unprofitable weeks with her grandmother at Romans had been, in the providence of God, a means of breaking the ties that bound her to Granne. She would not return there. She would go to the aunt who still had her house in Grenoble.

It was strange coming back to the city after an absence in which so many things had happened. Church spires and towers and clustering houses were as they had ever been. She saw on the hillsides the buildings of Ste Marie's as the carriage turned into the town. Men and women were going about their business much as they had always done. Yet their faces seemed the faces of strangers to her; she was an interloper who had deserted them and others had taken her place. There was an evil, hostile spirit in the city. It would be war, not peace, that awaited her there.

Her aunt welcomed her, and approved her plans.

"I think my old school friend Anne Brochier who was a Carmelite will join me," Philippine said. "I shall find a little lodging, somewhere quiet and poor, and we shall do needlework and sell it and earn enough to live on."

"Do you need to do that?" her aunt asked. "Your mother must have left you part of her estate."

"I have made over my share to my brother and sisters," said

Philippine. "I don't want a fortune. The best way to enjoy it is to give it up. I only want heavenly hopes for my portion. They have agreed to pay me a small annuity. Then what we make ourselves can be all spent on the poor."

"Well," said her aunt, "and what more?"

"We shall sell books—books on religion—they may help to bring the faith back to France."

"They may help to put you in prison," commented her aunt. "But I suppose you'd welcome that. They've turned Ste Marie's into a prison. It would be like going home for you."

"That would be too great an honour," answered Philippine. "But I think that there are plenty of my old friends and acquaintances still in Grenoble who would join me in trying to bring help to the men and women in captivity for their beliefs. You wait, we'll find a way of entering the darkest cells with food for body and soul."

Her aunt smiled.

"You'll bring a hornet's nest of criticism from the family about your ears," she remarked. "They'll accuse you of being so impossible that you couldn't get on with your grandmother, and now so pig-headed that you're deserting your father. You see if I'm not right. I know the family."

"The times are too desperate for half-measures, aren't they?" Philippine said.

"You believe that and will have to act in that belief," her aunt replied. "But don't expect everyone else to see eye to eye with you."

Philippine found her lodgings in a house by the quayside. The narrow streets round about were a warren where men and women crowded together and few questions were asked. It was cold and damp, and the icy winds of the blustering autumn blew through the timbers and snow piled up against the windows and doors. But from their garret window, Philippine and her companions could look up over the river to the heights of Rabot where Ste Marie's rested, and the sight gave them courage and inspiration.

No one would have recognized the novice of four years past in the bold-faced woman who climbed the hill and accosted the guards at the door of the old convent. One of themselves they took her to be, in her coarse skirt with a well-worn shawl about her shoulders. The cockade stuck in the kerchief over her head was a guarantee of her right revolutionary sentiments. She and her companion brought the men some of their provisions from the shops. She added a bottle of wine sometimes on her own account. If she wanted to look in at the prisoners in their cells, there was no harm in it. She had a way with her when she wanted anything that it was difficult to refuse. One of the jailors would go with her at first to show her the way and to show off his captives.

It nearly broke Philippine's heart in those first days to see Ste Marie's. When the outer door swung open, she stepped into a corridor filled with pikes and muskets, and foul with stale tobacco smoke. The garth at the end was overgrown with rank weeds, and grass straggled across the paths and hid the base of the cross. The cloister walls around were scrawled with the cries that the mob shouted, "Liberty", "Brotherhood", "Equality", and decorated with gross drawings that figured men's lowest cravings. In the chapel, the men of the National Guard lounged at their ease, drinking, smoking, playing cards. The unswept corridors were filthy with garbage left lying, and dust was thick on the windows. Some of the cells had been taken by the officers of the guard. In the room that had once been hers, a great burly man was sprawling on a truckle bed heaped high with the velvet altar hangings. Some of the smaller rooms were used for solitary confinement.

"But we don't waste time or space on solitary prisoners," the jailor told her with a laugh. "We put 'em all together—it helps to keep 'em warm. Now here you'll see what I mean."

He opened a door with the key he held. A hot breath of fetid air came out as Philippine looked in. It was a room that had once been a dormitory for the school children, a clean airy place where six little ones had been very happy. Now it held

F

more than twenty women, and its broken window panes had been stuffed with rags to keep out any fresh air that might have penetrated. Four or five slatternly women were occupying the centre of the room while two were brawling with each other.

"There you are, citoyenne," said the man with a chuckle. "You'd not recognize those grand ladies over there. See that one in the corner? She used to go about in a carriage and pair dressed up to the nines, with servants to wait on her." He suddenly shouted. "Hi, you over there, Mme de Brissac, stand up when you have visitors. And you other woman, what do they call you, de Chichiliane, take those dirty basins away and wash them."

He turned again to Philippine.

"That's the way to treat ladies of rank, citoyenne. Some like to call them without their titles. I say, much better fun to remind them of what they once were. But it's difficult to get a rise out of them. See that old party in the other corner? Peret her name is. She was a great one once. Founded the convent of Ursuline nuns. She's still got the remains of her habit, though you'd hardly recognize it in those old rags that she's wearing."

He spat in her direction. Philippine felt sick as he shut the door again. But her task was not completed. She forced herself to laugh as he went on the rounds. Among the men, she found there were priests. It was both joy and sorrow to discover Fr Ravenas of their number. He did not recognize her on her first coming, but when she had so managed that the soldiers took her visits as a matter of course, she spoke to him.

"I wish I could put you again a free man among the mountains of the Drôme," she said.

He shook his head.

"My soul has never been so free as here behind prison bars," he said. "The best of Lovers is with me."

Philippine burst out, "And I—I am left still in the world—I should by now have been a professed nun—and I am nothing."

The priest shook his head again.

"You are very pleasing to your Divine Lover—He has not left you. His Heart is not weak and impatient like ours. Trust Him, my child."

The men and women she served cautioned her. The work she did was dangerous; at the least, it was exhausting.

"It's the least we can do," she said as she gave the contents of her basket of provisions to the prisoners. "If I may not suffer with you, I must minister to those who are more worthy. How else can I prove my love for God?"

She brought them news from the outside world. They would pray for the Queen riding with her hands bound behind her, clad in her muslin dress, in the tumbril that took her through the Paris streets in the October drizzle, to die at noon. They would pray for the priests who for fear of their lives had given in to the Committee of Public Safety. They would pray for the men and women who were seizing Church property and melting down bells for cannon, for the mad devotees who had enthroned the Goddess of Reason in Notre Dame, placing an opera singer where Our Lady had stood. They would pray for the success of the stand being made at Toulon against the Terror. There might be hopes there that, though Marseilles and Lyons had fallen to the Jacobins, Toulon, with its garrison of Royalists in touch with an English squadron without, might prove impregnable and so remain a springboard for the reconquest of France by forces of more moderate ideas. But one day in December, as Philippine entered the prison, the guards greeted her with shouts of triumph.

"Have you a bottle with you to-day, citoyenne?" one man asked, and as she took one from her basket, he poured it out and gave a toast.

"Long live the Revolution! The news to-day wants something to wash it down. You've not heard yet? Toulon has fallen at last. Ah, Barras got 'em down. He knows how to choose his men. They say he's got a grand lad with him—what did they say his name was?"

"Bonaparte," prompted another soldier, taking his turn at

the bottle. "They say he's quite young—twenty-four or five—
but he knows all there is to know about artillery. And what his
cannons didn't do, the guillotine has done. They've tumbled a
few heads into the basket, I can tell you. That old General de
Saussure who used to be here—he's one of 'em. Long live the
Revolution!"

Philippine felt numbed with anxiety. The future now
would be reddened with blood.

So it was. The Terror spread, increasing in its ferocity. No
one could be safe, for at any moment might come denunciation
as a suspect. Ste Marie's was filled to overflowing. Execution
was the easiest way of emptying its cells. As she had anticipated,
there were many valiant women to join her in her work of
bringing temporal and spiritual help to the prisoners. There
were some who had been religious—Carmelites, Ursulines,
Nuns of the Visitation—some who had merely drifted through
a comfortable existence before the basis of all that they held
precious had been undermined, and who now realized their
Christian dignity when the trappings of fashion had gone. They
hid hunted priests in their own homes, they went abroad visiting the prisons and tending the sick, they risked their lives to
attend the secret Masses offered in lonely places at midnight.
With such a leader to inspire them as Philippine Duchesne, they
were ready for anything. Her dearest joy, when she had said her
prayers and finished her work, was to climb the hill and be shut
into the same foul rooms as the martyrs of Christ.

One day she found Fr Ravenas and his friend Joseph
Guillabert as happy as if they had been invited to a feast.
The guard, as he opened the door to her, touched his forehead
significantly.

"Cracked, that's what they are, citoyenne. They're off to-
morrow."

"Off to-morrow?" Philippine asked. "Have they been set
free?"

"I should say so!" the man sneered. "No, they're off to
Paris, to the cellars of the Conciergerie. And after that, it'll be

Mme la Guillotine they'll be calling on. Though why they couldn't just as easily lose their heads in Grenoble and save the expense of the journey, beats me."

The room looked different when she entered. A streak of spring sunlight was coming through the window high up in the wall. There were faces she did not know among the prisoners, and faces she knew were missing. The priest greeted her with a radiant smile.

"What changes have taken place, my child, in the last fortnight," he exclaimed. He looked closely at her. She was weeping silently. "Why, you aren't going to make me sad by your sorrow?" he asked gently, and as she still did not answer him, he added, "It's a great grace, isn't it, to die for the faith? I thought you wished me well—you're not going to grieve over my happiness?"

Philippine's hands dropped from her face.

'Oh no, Father," she cried, "just the opposite. I envy your happiness so much—that's why I'm grieving—because I cannot die for Our Lord too."

Fr Ravenas smiled again and said, "Oh, then I'm quite satisfied and pleased with you. Listen, Fr Guillabert here has had a great grace—he heard to-day that some of his friends had had a Mass offered up secretly for him."

"It's true," said the second priest. "I was fearful when I first heard that we were to be taken to Paris, but now it is different. The Blood of the Lamb offered up for me makes me ashamed of hesitating to shed mine. I have strength now from that Holy Sacrifice to carry me on until I enter into Eternal Life."

"Bless Our Lord with us," Fr Ravenas said. "We want to give Him back life for life and love for love."

"And I?" asked Philippine, the tears still in her eyes.

"You must give Him your life and your love. When we are gone, you must help to supply our loss—you can give the Word of Truth and Life—you must help to feed the sheep and the lambs of Our Lord."

When she returned that evening to her lodgings, Anne

Brochier was waiting in some anxiety. She had been visiting their sick.

"It's old Susanne," she said. "I don't think she will last long. She's asking at last for a priest. I have one ready to bring to her, but it's impossible to take him to her rooms—the house is full of Jacobins. What shall we do?"

"Do?" asked Philippine. "Why, you must go as quickly as you can to my cousin, Mme de Savoie Rollin, and get her man Jules to bring the handcart round. We'll put old Susanne on it—I'll fetch some coverlets—and we'll take her to our own rooms."

That night a priest slipped into the garret room of the house by the river. When he left, old Susanne was quiet in the bed where she lay. She pulled the bedclothes close over her.

"It's cold," she mumbled.

Philippine and Anne were on their knees beside her. Poor soul, she would need much prayer after the life she had led. Thank God she had made her peace with Him at the end. The woman's hand groped over the counterpane.

"I'm afraid," she whispered. Philippine rose, and put her arm about her. The old woman seemed to fall asleep. The two prayed on while the stars dimmed in the sky and the grey walls of Ste Marie's, glimpsed through their window, turned rosy with the rising sun. Old Susanne opened her eyes. She smiled, and settled back against Philippine.

"I'm so glad you came—Mother—" she said, and died as quietly as a child falling asleep.

Anne Brochier thought, "She went back to her childhood —to the best of her life. She took Philippine's arms for the arms that used to shelter her—a mother's arms—a beautiful mistake. I wonder—was it a mistake?"

11: *Time Passes*

FATHER Ravenas died joyfully on the scaffold on 26 June 1794. On 29 June, while the crowd shouted "Down with the tyrant!" and cursed with a wild delight, Robespierre, a bloodstained bandage about his jaw shattered by his ineffective attempt to kill himself, knelt beneath the same knife in miserable acceptance of the inevitable.

The cries of the crowd were taken up through the length and breadth of France. Everywhere men who had been sickened by the Terror revived their hopes and came out again into the open. The prisons began emptying. There was a renewed demand for a Constitution that would give peace at home and security abroad.

Philippine found her work in Ste Marie's at an end. Life in Grenoble began to be more normal. The evil spirit was retreating. The faces of men and women became more friendly, more human. Shops opened and clusters of people gossiped again without fear of who might hear their words. The Périers came back to their house and M. Duchesne followed suit. Mélanie folded back shutters in unfamiliar rooms and took off dust-covers from furniture and ornaments that had shrunk from her memories of them. She explored a Grenoble that was a new place to her, untouched by the ghosts of former days that her sisters knew. Things had changed and she belonged to the new France that was shaping itself out of the chaos. Dauphiné wanted to do her part. Claude Périer, with his sound financial ideas, would be a man to send to the legislative assembly in Paris. His brother and his brother-in-law, Pierre François Duchesne, would be equally useful. There would be no more of the happy carefree family life between the two houses now. Philippine refused to return home. She must keep her independence, must be free to follow her own ideas, to do whatever God showed He wanted from her. The family grumbled, criticized. She would not enter again into arguments. Having put her hand to the plough, she would not turn back.

"But times have changed so," Mme de Mauduit said. "You'll never get a chance of becoming a nun again. The Directory can't make up its mind whether it is going to let even priests come back again—it will and it won't—and you can't trust it an inch—look at the way it has deported those that did return. That's what will happen for years to come—and by that time you will be an old woman and beyond hope of a match."

"I'm twenty-seven now," Philippine laughed. "Give up that hope, Amélie."

"Frédéric de Saussure has come back from England," Amélie said. "He's not married yet. And his mother has died. He was telling me how she asked to be buried among Catholics in London and she lies now in a corner of St Pancras churchyard. I think that shows good feeling in her son—he does not believe, you know."

"So he would make an excellent match for me," said Philippine.

"I thought your apostolic zeal might count for something," retorted her sister. "You can't go converting heathens in foreign parts when the English fleets hold the high seas and not a French vessel can put out from port."

"I might join an order in another country," said Philippine. "I might be a Carmelite if I couldn't get into a Visitation Convent."

"You're not likely to manage that wild-goose scheme," countered Mme de Mauduit. "You are much too young to plan to go abroad like that. Why, can't you see that this General Bonaparte will be making things impossible for Frenchmen to escape from France—he'll have all Europe beneath our sway if he goes on winning victories at the rate he has begun. He's a man with a colossal will, my husband says."

"And yet he is only twenty-seven too," Philippine reflected.

"Well, then what do you mean to do?" asked Amélie de Mauduit.

"What I'm doing now," said Philippine. "There are still priests in the city prison, there are still poor people to be nursed and still arrangements to be made for secret Masses and priests to hide. I've still my prayers to say and my rule to keep. I belong to Grenoble. I'm not going to run away again. I shall wait."

Up on the hillside, Ste Marie's was waiting. Seven years were a little space of time in its two centuries of life. But seven years were much when each day of them had to be lived in uncertainty of the future. Waiting was not easy.

The evil spirit did not wait. With the backing of the army, the Directory felt strong enough to attack the fountain head of Catholicism. In December 1797, the eighty-year-old Pius VI was endeavouring to maintain an unquiet peace when the agents of the Directory assembled more than three hundred malcontents at the Trinità dei Monti, in the Villa Medici. They were plied with wine and then burst out into the Eternal City with cries of "Long live Liberty!" The twenty-ninth of December was a day of confusion and rioting. It was the beginning of a campaign of terror which each day brought more and more French troops into Rome until, on 15 February 1798, the Directory could seize all temporal power and proclaim the foundation of the Roman Republic.

Then came news of outrage after outrage offered to the Holy Father.

"It makes one's heart swell with pride," said Philippine, "to hear what they say. He won't wear the tricolour of the Revolution though they offered him safety with it. 'We know no in-signia but those with which the Church invests us,' he said. 'You have all power over our body; none over our soul!' There's a Swiss Calvinist, Haller, in charge of him—a man of gross feelings who treats the old man more harshly than a criminal."

"The news to-day is worse," said Anne Brochier. "They have made him go from Rome—they are sending him from one place to another—a prisoner with only a few attendants. Fortunately one is Fr Marotti who used to be a Jesuit."

"Ah," said Philippine, "I thought a son of St Ignatius wouldn't desert him."

"They say that is what the Holy Father said when he asked Fr Marotti if he had enough courage to follow him to Calvary, and the Jesuit answered that he had," Anne replied. "His guards won't let him stay long anywhere, but the princes in Italy and the common people are all welcoming him—even the English minister at Florence has offered his respects."

It was a relief to know that the Pope was permitted at last to stay in a monastery outside Florence. But there could be no planning for a future of religious life when the French government held the Head of the Church a prisoner. Philippine had to go on from day to day doing what came nearest to her hand and praying in blind trust. Seventeen ninety-eight passed with its hopes and fears, its dividing loyalties when the only hope for the Church seemed to be in the defeat of France. Grenoble's citizens were buoyed up with the success of Napoleon in the east, cast down by Nelson's victory at the Battle of the Nile, cheered by the French conquest of Switzerland, depressed by the bad news that came with the closing year and the fresh spring. The French armies had lost their positions on the Rhine, and the armies in Italy were everywhere suffering defeat. The Directory ordered the removal of Pius VI.

"They are bringing him across the Alps," Mme Périer said to her niece. "He is a dying man, but they care nothing for that. These early days of May are cold and yet they will do nothing for him. Thank God the mountaineers have come forward to show him love and ask his blessing. The commissary is keeping him at Briançon—please God they let him die there in peace."

But when twenty-five days had passed, the tide of war came nearer to the frontiers of France and the order again came that the Pope was to leave instantly, dead or alive. They found a mail wagon, little better than a cart, and took him along the road through Savines, where the only shelter he was allowed was the miserable cottage of a peasant, through Drac to Cors and Lamur.

"He'll be at Vizille by 5 July," said Mme Périer. "I am leaving Grenoble to give him a fit welcome there. The château can be once again a shelter for Liberty—the only true liberty, though now it is a prisoner."

"We can't have so much enthusiasm being shown," said the administrators in Grenoble, as they fingered the money paid them by the Maréchale of Vaux in order to be allowed to give the Holy Father hospitality the following day. "He must be brought into the city by night."

In the mild darkness of the night of 6 July, the few carriages of the Pope's suite and his guards approached Grenoble. The dusky forms of the mountains reared up behind, quiet and steadfast. But the stillness was broken near the city by tumultuous cheers from the people ranged in double rows by the roadside. They fell on their knees as the carriage passed, then turned back with it.

"Close the city gates," ordered the commissary, but it was too late. The crowds without were met by the crowds within and Pius VI entered the capital of Dauphiné like a conqueror.

For five days the men and women of Grenoble showed the commandant and guards that faith was not dead. The commissary could do nothing to prevent them approaching and showing their joy at seeing Christ's Vicar. Time after time, Pius VI gave them his blessing, a frail old man in white whose word alone could prevent the soldiers from being violently treated.

"It makes you think of the soldiers in the Garden of Geth-semane," remarked Anne Brochier. "They only had power be-cause Our Lord willed it. We could easily overwhelm these—only the Holy Father says they are doing their duty and he per-mits them to keep him captive. I got into the house to-day as a serving girl, and waited on him."

"Even the guards here are asking his blessing," said Philip-pine. "How can we creep along in the service of God when we see him striding along so valiantly? Oh, Anne, I can't give up hope that one day you and I will get back to our religious life in our convents—here is Calvary but the Resurrection follows."

On 10 July, the commissary hurried the Pope to his carriage, but there could be no hurrying once they were in the roads. Everywhere the people crowded to see him go, weeping and praying and asking for his blessing. At the prison the horses were stopped, and men besought the old man to give a special benediction to the priests still within. As Pius VI raised his hand, Philippine, on her knees with the rest, saw it, as it were, pointing to where on the heights of Rabot Ste Marie's stood desolate.

Valence lay ahead. Beyond Valence, the Directory saw Dijon as the final prison. But the thoughts of men are not God's and in the night between 28 and 29 August Pius VI died, at the age of eighty-one.

"I am thirty to-day," Philippine reflected. "Nearly half my allotted span of life gone and nothing to show for it."

Anne Brochier thought, "What are years in the design of God? The Holy Father has ruled the Church twenty-four years—longer than any other pontiff—yet the greatness of his life has been perfected in these last months of suffering."

In Paris, Claude Périer was amassing a fortune by his able economy and laying the foundations of the Bank of France; Pierre François Duchesne, presiding at meetings of the depu-ties, was growing more and more uncertain of the progress of liberalism under new tyrannies; Sieyès was on the look out for a general strong enough to enforce the will of a few chosen politicians. In the east, Napoleon Bonaparte had made his last arrangements. That done, he was not one to delay. While others were still disputing, he arrived on 9 October at Fréjus and all eyes in France turned to him. The Jacobin Club of Grenoble sent him an address. He read and noted its contents. On the fatal 9th of November, when he had left the Assembly in Paris with his full acceptance as the man who would deliver France from the Directory still uncertain, he saw the troops drawn up in the mild thin sunshine, and the dramatic moment burst upon him. The words the men of Dauphiné had used rose to his lips and he cried: "What have you done with this France that I left so brilliant? I left you peace, and I find war. I left you victory and I find defeats. I left you the millions of Italy and I find laws of spoliation and misery!" Enthusiastically the troops rallied to him, and when the fog crept up from the Seine over the midnight city, the Directory was no more and France had a Consul to lead her to internal peace.

By May 1800, Philippine found there were no more priests to visit in prison.

"Perhaps you'll settle down now to a reasonable life," said her grandmother. "Amélie and Charlotte will be glad of your help to bring up their children."

"I don't think that is what God wants of me," replied Philippine.

"What do you mean to do then?" snapped old Mme Duchesne. "You'll not find a convent now that will take you— even if they do reopen, as seems likely under this new upstart from Corsica who apparently thinks that it will be more profitable to make a concordat with Rome. Whose advice do you mean to take if you won't listen to your family?"

"Why, I'm going to consult St Francis Regis, if you want to know," answered Philippine. "I wished to go to his shrine seven years ago when we were at Granne, but Father and Mother wouldn't let me."

"I should think not," said Mme Duchesne. "A young girl like you trapesing twelve leagues across country to La Louvesc."

"But as I'm not young now, I'm going," said Philippine.

She set off next day with one of her grandmother's servants. As she went over the rough roads and through the isolated mountain villages, she saw again the Jesuit saint treading those same paths nearly two centuries before her. She thought of him gathering the lost sheep of his Lord's flock, tending the sick and teaching the children. She remembered how he had longed to be sent to the Canadian missions, to labour and maybe die for the conversion of the Hurons and Iroquois, and how he had found his mission field instead in his own native land. The life that was brimming over in the fields and on the mountain slopes filled her heart with fresh life—birds, flowers, trees, the very streams swollen with the melting snows, spoke of renewal. St Francis Regis would show her the way she was to take.

"It's a good day to arrive," remarked Philippine to her companion. "The third of May—the Invention of the Holy Cross."

The cross had marked the shrine. As she stood at the open door of the church, she could see only the empty tomb of the saint—his body had been removed to safety away from the fury of the revolutionaries. Around it, the watchful angels were broken and maimed, the altar covered with dust, and strewn with the debris of another altar that had been wrecked. It was mournful and desolate, a place for sorrowing, where the Holy Sacrifice of the Altar could no longer be offered. The servant touched her sleeve.

"They're saying Mass in the barn yonder," he said.

She joined the crowds that thronged into the shed. Faith was alive. The living angels gathered there in their countless bands, and St Francis Regis's soul was more present than his body. Philippine was on the outskirts of the crowd. It was impossible to get near the improvised altar rails for Holy Communion.

"I'll wait until Mass is over," she said. Was waiting to be always her lot? But when the men and women had gone and

She found her way barred by a group of ragged boys. . .

the priest gave her the Bread of Life, she felt content with a peace that was more than thrilling consolations. To wait, when God was at the end of your waiting—how could you repine? Now that she had St Francis Regis for her intercessor she must get back quickly to Grenoble and begin work. She must delay no longer.

As she came back to her lodgings in the city, she found her way barred by a group of ragged boys. Yelling and sparring, they filled the road with their clamour. As she paused, they gave way and then turned and followed her begging for a crust or a coin. She gave them what she had, and turned into her house.

"There is my work," she told herself. "That is what the saint advises me to do. Like him, I will care for the neglected children of France."

12: *The Return*

"ALL right," said Philippine on Whit Sunday 1801. "That's very good. One more question and then we'll have the *brioches*. Who gave the Catholic Church divine authority to teach?"

The dozen or so urchins seated at her feet on the floor burst out laughing.

"Oh, Mlle Duchesne, that isn't half an easy one—you're always asking us that."

"Well?" said Philippine. "What's the answer? You, René, stop pulling Jean's hair and tell me."

"Jesus Christ," René answered glibly, "when He said, 'Go ye and teach all nations.' And are we going to have jam with them?"

"Of course," said Philippine, going over to her cupboard. René leant forward and encompassing Antoine and Henri with his arms, knocked their heads together from sheer delight.

"Ow! you brute!" Henri yelled good naturedly, punching back with all his might, while Daniel kicked at the struggling group indiscriminately. In a corner, Pierre was sparring with Paul amid the rapturous hoots of the onlookers. Philippine turned on them with a plate piled high with food.

"Sit down quietly, all of you," she ordered. There was immediate peace. "Now, Jean, you can pass the *brioches* round."

"And will you tell us a story, Mlle Duchesne?" René demanded.

"About the Red Indians," François suggested, with his mouth full.

"And scalping and torturing," said Daniel, licking some jam from his hand.

"I like the one about Fr Daniel being shot through with arrows."

"René Goupil's better," boasted René. "They tomahawked him and he cried out 'Jesus!' and didn't yell a bit."

Pierre had secured a second *brioche*.

"I like the way they bit off Fr Jogues's fingers," he said, munching happily.

"Fr de Brébœuf's best," Paul decided. "Tell us that one, Mlle Duchesne—about how he died."

"Well," said Philippine, "the Indians took him prisoner at last, and they tied him up to a stake and then they put burning hatchets round his neck like a necklace. They couldn't draw a cry from him and all the time he went on telling them about God and about His love for their souls, and he turned to the others who were being tortured with him and said, 'Lift up your eyes to heaven. Let us die in this faith. Bear with courage these few remaining tortures—the glory which follows will never have an end.' And then they tore his heart out—"

The door suddenly burst open and two more boys fell into the room. The older one held the smaller by the neckband of a very torn jacket. His captive looked round like a wild animal, his eyes resting suspiciously at last on Philippine.

"Got him!" said his captor triumphantly. "I told him you'd give him some spice bread if he came, and a new shirt—he didn't want the shirt but he's that eager for the cake—here, don't you be making off, there's the lady I told you about."

The ragged little lad burst into tears.

"I don't want to go to school—I don't want to say any prayers—my dad says they ain't no good—and my mum'll wallop me."

G

"All right," said Philippine. "No one's going to make you come here or say prayers if you don't want to. Here, Jean, give him a *brioche* while I get some spice bread. And the rest of you, sing the hymn to Our Lady we learnt yesterday and then be off with you."

While she saw that the newcomer was fed, the boys stood up, crumby and well smeared with jam, and, with more energy than modulation, sang through the five verses of the hymn she had taught them. The boy munched his spice bread in silence at a safe distance from Philippine, watching, with quick glances from boys to teacher. With the last notes, babel broke out again.

"So long, Mlle Duchesne! Goodbye! Finish the story next time! Those *brioches* were grand! So long!"

They pushed each other through the door, there was the noise of an avalanche descending the stairs, then the outer door was slammed and the street was filled with catcalls and laughter. Only the stranger was left.

"Well?" asked Philippine. "Can you manage another slice?"

The boy shook his head. He pulled his ragged jacket over his chest and muttered something.

"What?" asked Philippine, bending her head close to hear. "Of course you can have the shirt too. It'll make you very smart. What about having a good wash before you put it on?"

She brought a basin and superintended the washing. Jacket off, it was a pitiful bony little chest that was revealed.

"Underfed," thought Philippine. "Underfed, body and soul."

She bandaged up a sore on his arm, and then helped him to slip into the shirt she had ready for just such an occasion. He wriggled into it, warm and proud.

"Eh! I'll be coming again," he said, making for the door.

"All right," Philippine called out after his retreating form. She went back to clear up the mess, but before she had got far in her work, the door burst open again. On the threshold, arms akimbo, face red, stood her landlady.

"Now, Mlle Duchesne, I'll not stand this sort of thing any longer. I'm just fed up with this, week after week. Making my house filthy with their trapesing into it—that's bad enough, but it isn't half so bad as all the noise. I won't stand it, I say. All the complaints that I have to put up with—I'll be losing my other lodgers—mine's a respectable house, I'd have you know —and you make it a bear garden—if you must run a school, why in the name of all the saints and angels don't you have little girls?"

"The little girls of Grenoble have quite enough schools," answered Philippine dryly. "And if I can put up with the noise and dirt of the boys at close quarters, I think others can, too, at a distance. However, I suppose I can take myself elsewhere— I'd rather have these boys learning their catechism and making their confession and Holy Communion than be enjoying the good opinion of the other people in the house."

"Now don't take it amiss, Mlle Duchesne," the woman replied, anxious lest she should depart. "I don't want you to leave —everybody knows you're really all right—with your father a deputy and your rich friends and all—but it's the noise!"

"Then you'll have to try to be patient about that," said Philippine, glancing over the landlady's head. Another woman was coming up the stairs, a thin, slatternly creature, followed by a big burly man.

"You're Mlle Duchesne?" the woman asked truculently.

"I am," said Philippine.

"Well, then, you'll have the goodness to stop teaching our Paul the nonsense you are—if you don't, my husband'll want to know the reason why."

"Yes, why," echoed the man.

"Why what?" asked Philippine a bit mystified.

"Telling him he shouldn't work on Sundays, indeed! My husband fair skinned him when he gave us a bit of lip last Sunday."

"Fair skinned him, I did," the man repeated, with obvious satisfaction.

"But he came to Mass to-day," Philippine said, remembering how Paul had kept his word.

"Ay, he did and why? 'Because Mlle Duchesne said I should.' That's all we got out of him. So, Mlle Duchesne, you'll stop teaching him that kind of rot, or we'll know the reason why."

"Yes," the man re-echoed, "the reason why."

"Very good," said Philippine, watching the man's big fist. "The reason why is that it's the law of God. Now, what are you going to say?"

The woman faltered. The man opened his mouth and shut it again without saying anything.

"All right," Philippine went on, "as there's nothing further to say, good-day."

They went down the stairs, muttering and threatening, while step by step the landlady followed them and shut the door upon them. Philippine sighed.

"What's the good of going on?" she thought. "So few people care about their own souls or the souls of others. It's self, self, self. Well, it wasn't self with St Francis Regis. If he could go on in spite of discouragement, I'll have a try too."

She finished her work and went off to see Anne Brochier. There were two friends with her, young women who had been Carmelites ten years before.

"Shall we ever get back to our convents?" one asked. "Will religious life ever again be found in France?"

"I think it will," said Philippine. "But we'll have to pray for it. I've been saying the collect of St Bruno for years so that his sons can come back to the Grande Chartreuse."

"Prayer, yes, but suffering, too, is needed, I think," said the other.

Philippine was standing by the window.

"Do you see up there—the roofs of Ste Marie's," Anne pointed out. "It belongs to the people now—"

"So they say," Philippine answered. "But we are the people. Oh, Anne, suppose we could get it back again for the service of God! The Visitation nuns could return to their old quarters and you Carmelites could have the chaplain's old house."

"And then we'd all wake up," said Anne sadly. "No, Philippine, it won't happen like that. We'll have to wait for the hand of God."

"Wait!" said Philippine. "But I think God sometimes means us to set our own hand to the task. We might find some way to return there if only we searched hard enough."

The others laughed at her eagerness, but Philippine grew silent as the longing to be once more within the walls of Ste Marie's seized upon her. She said a hasty goodbye and in the afternoon called on her own home. Mélanie threw her arms round her with joy.

"It's a lovely day, Philippine. Can't we go for a walk?" she said. "And we could take Baby Amélie. Do say yes."

Mme de Mauduit put on her little daughter's bonnet and pelisse, and saw them off.

"Don't take them too far," she cautioned. "I know what you are, Philippine. You think everyone can do as much as you."

"I can carry Amélie if she gets tired," said fourteen-year-old Aunt Mélanie, and they set off.

"Let's go up the hill to Ste Marie's," Mélanie urged.

In the hot sunshine of the Whitsun afternoon, many of the citizens of Grenoble were taking the air. They drifted up to the old convent. Seated on chairs set out by the caretaker, they sipped wine and cut at hunks of bread and cheese with jack-knives while they looked across the valley at the chain of mountain peaks misty in the heat. Guffaws of laughter sounded where once the novices kept monastic silence.

"Strange," thought Philippine, "that I should be up here to-day. I didn't plan this. I wonder if one really does have to wait for the Hand of God to reveal itself."

"Do look at Amélie!" exclaimed Mélanie, turning with a laugh to her sister. "She's a sharp little thing for three, isn't she?"

The child had gone across the terrace by herself, toddling firmly until she reached the rank grass that had overgrown the playground of the children. With a chuckle, she rolled over and buried herself in the green coolness.

"What's she saying?" asked Mélanie, laughing, too, at the sight of her delight. Amélie came face upwards still chuckling. Philippine bent forward to catch her words.

"Oh, yes, oh yes," Amélie was saying. "I shall come to school here. And I shall make my First Communion here."

"Isn't she cute?" said Mélanie. "Where on earth did she pick that up from? I'm sure she doesn't know anything about school or First Communion."

Philippine did not answer. Was this the Hand of God showing at last?

"My God," she prayed with a sudden keen pain, "let the child's words come true."

That evening she made her plans. St Francis Regis was to be honoured. He would help her then to buy back Ste Marie's.

"Boys," she told her ragamuffins, "you've got to pray for all you're worth that I shall see what God wants me to do and how to do it."

She went off to the Vicar General.

"Shall I go on with this?" she asked.

"God's finger is in it," he assured her.

She wrote to Reverend Mother de Murinais without delay and with her drew up a petition to the administrator of the department. Everything had been done now. She would get an answer and then proceed. But no answer came. Days and weeks sped by. What was the petition of an ex-novice and a nun of eighty?

"We'll go on praying," Philippine urged her boys. For the moment she had enough to occupy her. Her cousin's husband, M. de Rollin, was dangerously ill, and she was helping to nurse him. There was something in her own vitality that seemed to put fresh life into him.

"What can I do to repay you for all you have done for me?"

Mme de Rollin asked when at length her husband was safely convalescing.

In a flash, Philippine knew the answer.

"The only thing that would give me pleasure would be if your husband would use his influence to get Ste Marie's for me."

"Of course he shall," answered Mme de Rollin. "And my father and Uncle Casimir. They're both in Paris now and can do something."

Still nothing came. But Philippine had another ally. Each day she visited a poor man who needed nursing. He joined her in a forty-days' prayer. On the last day of it, she received a message, asking her to go to the prefecture.

"Mlle Duchesne," said the Prefect, "I have to tell you that the house once called Ste Marie d'en Haut is to be yours on payment of a yearly sum of 800 francs and on condition that you put it into a state of proper repair."

"What!" cried Philippine. "God has given it back to us at last! When can I take possession of it?"

The Prefect smiled to see her delight.

"It's yours as from 10 December," he said, "but you can't possibly go into it. It's in a disgusting state of dirt and disrepair. It will take weeks to get it straight. You must wait a bit."

"Wait! I've been waiting over ten years," Philippine said. "I shall go into it now without any delay."

"I'll go and tell my ally," she thought as she left the prefecture. "He's the representative of my Master. He must be the first to share my joy."

She hurried to the sick man's garret room.

"We must thank God together," she said and laughed with happiness to see his pleasure.

It was different when she went back home to tell the good news.

"You're quite mad," said Mme Jouve. "How do you think the convent is going to exist, even if you can get the other nuns to come back? It won't be Holy Poverty, but unholy beggary you'll be practising."

"Why on earth can't you wait till Easter?" asked Mme de Mauduit. "The place is almost in ruins, and in this weather it'll be the death of all of you."

"Are you quite sure you have taken enough advice?" was Mme de Rollin's comment. "Things are still so unsettled, you may get driven out again before you know where you are."

"Think what you all like," said Philippine. "I'm going at once. Do you think I am going to delay an hour when I've been sighing for this so many years? It's high time to show the world what lies it has been telling when it said that nuns were poor enslaved victims—it'll see now how glad we are to return to our home."

Back in her lodgings she began her packing. Presently there was a knock at her door.

"A priest to see you," said the landlady, and Fr Rivet was there, smiling, with hand outstretched.

"Mlle Duchesne! I've just heard your good news," he said. "And I've come to add more to it. The Concordat between the Holy Father and our First Consul Bonaparte has been agreed upon. It looks as if there will be peace for your work at Ste Marie's."

"You come like a messenger from Our Lord," she said, happy again. His visit was like one in return for her morning's visit to the sick man.

There was plenty to do in the next four days. The letters she wrote to the dispersed nuns and to Reverend Mother de Murinais could not get to them in time. Only Mother Faucherand lived near enough to join her. "But it will be all right," thought Philippine joyously. "I'll take Delphine Blanchard with me—poor child, without father or mother, she has nowhere to go."

The fourteenth of December was chill and wet. By the afternoon everything had been packed. Twelve-year-old Delphine went off to meet Mother Faucherand. With cheers

Through the gathering dark they climbed the hill.

and laughter, the catechism class arrived for the last time at the house. Each boy seized a bundle. Through the gathering dark they climbed the hill, and Philippine followed their noisy progress, and went once more through the gateway that shut off her loved convent from the world. It was a homecoming at last—a happy return though the place was ruinous.

"Ow!" laughed Paul, setting down his load as the porter at the lodge let them in. "I got a river down my neck. But your things haven't got wet."

"I'm as soaked as if I'd fallen into the Isère," remarked René. "You could squeeze me out and hang me up to dry."

"There you are," said Daniel, "all your things, Mlle Duchesne—we've not pinched a single thing."

He paused. They looked at her, a circle of eager young faces lit by the flickering lamp.

"It's goodbye now," thought Philippine, her heart aching more than she had expected. They were still waiting.

"Please, Mlle," Jean began, "won't we ever be able to see you again?"

"Not as you have been," said Philippine. Would they understand her if she spoke to them of the bond that prayer would make, and the inward vision that was better than the sight of the eyes?

"Come on, boys," Paul said gruffly. "Goodbye, Mlle Duchesne. It'll be all right—we'll see you again in heaven."

They moved off into the rain and the darkness, their cries of "Goodbye, Mlle Duchesne!" growing fainter and fainter.

"Aren't you ever coming in, Sister Duchesne?" called Mother Faucherand from the end of the corridor.

There was much to do that evening unpacking the bedding and cleaning out a few rooms that they could use until the place was ready. Mother Faucherand found it cold, and Delphine was afraid of the slanting shadows that ran up and down the old walls as they walked, lantern-lit, along the echoing corridors. Philippine swept and dusted, and got together a meal, her heart singing with joy. At last bedtime came. While the other two went to their rooms, she hastened to the chapel. The door at the end was swinging loose on its hinges. As she lifted her lantern, she saw the sleeting rain blowing through three broken windows. The stalls and benches were chipped and covered with dust, but at the far end the altar still stood, though the tabernacle was empty.

"All these years with no one giving You Your meed of love and worship here, dear Lord," she thought. Her pulse quickened. "Ah, but to-night I will be here to praise You for Your goodness and thank You for Your Mercies! I will give You love for love—I who have waited so many years for this moment. I will be here all the night through upon my knees, glorying in all that You have done for me."

A hand came out from the shadows behind her, and took hold of her arm.

"Sister Duchesne," said Mother Faucherand, "do come along quickly. I just can't sleep all by myself to-night. Won't you bring your bed into my room? I'm afraid to be alone."

Philippine sighed. She looked back into the darkness of the chapel, and then at the terrified nun clutching her arm.

"Very well," she said, and went along with her.

13: My Thoughts are not Your Thoughts

"TEN days to Christmas!" said Philippine. "We'll have everything ready by then for the coming of Our Lord."

Mother Faucherand might go about in a permanent shawl, the two or three other nuns who had come back might shiver as the wind howled through the broken windows; she was so happy that it was a real joy to sweep away the snow, and clear the rubbish from the rooms, and urge the workmen on in their repairs, and cook the meals for the little community. It was a bit disappointing to find refusals coming from some of their old companions who had already taken up their religious life in convents in other lands.

"Never mind," said Philippine, as they sat in a small room round a fire at night in the midst of the vast empty building. "We'll be fit to welcome the Holy Child as proper nuns on Christmas Day."

She pulled out a large bale of black material.

"What are you going to do with that?" asked one of the nuns.

"It's what you are going to do," Philippine answered. "Come and help. We'll make habits so that we can be clothed again in our right livery."

"For God's sake, be careful," said Mother Faucherand,

nervously. "You know habits are not to be worn by law. We'll be getting into trouble."

But Philippine only laughed at her fears, and the others, catching fire from her enthusiasm, turned to with a right good will, until by the time the light had faded from the winter sky on Christmas Eve, the habits were ready to be worn.

"We'll have to get them blessed," said Philippine. "We can't have Mass in the chapel here, but I've spoken to a priest in the town."

One of the workmen lingered behind.

"You good ladies will be going down to Midnight Mass?" he asked. "I'll be honoured to light you on your way."

"You are still a believer in spite of the Revolution?" Philippine said.

"Surely," answered the workman. "When you've been a lay-brother, as I have, in the Grande Chartreuse, you can't forget God. I'm living for the day when I can go back into the silence and solitude of the mountains and forests, and find Him and serve Him in prayer and praise."

"Strange," said Philippine, "I have been praying for you all these years, and yet it's I who have come home first."

In the dark, following the flickering light of the workman's lantern, the little band stumbled down the hill, each with her habit in a parcel. At the church the priest took them into the sacristy and in secret blessed each one. At the Midnight Mass that followed, Philippine was lighthearted with joy.

"Dear Holy Child," she prayed, "You have given us a present worthy of Your Majesty."

What did it matter that her habit was still only the habit of a novice? Soon, soon, the life of Ste Marie's would be resumed in all its vigour and God would take her as His very own.

Holy priests got to know of their doings up on the hillside. The chapel was soon fit for Mass, with its spotless altar and the tribute of linen and candles, though there were draughts still in the choir stalls where broken panes let in the weather. Men and women admitted to the services wept with joy to see what had been done to restore God's worship and begged Philippine to accept their offerings of money to hasten on her work.

"Why must they speak to you each time?" asked Mother Faucherand acidly.

"I suppose because my name appeared on the deed that restored the convent to our order," said Philippine. She had just been reading some letters from three former nuns, pointing out to her that they thought her actions precipitate. Perhaps they did seem so to those who were not on the spot. If they were, they would be as ready as she was to risk things. God would be their reward as He was hers. And what did it matter if she was only a novice, provided that God's work was done? They must want things set to rights. It just happened that she was actually there to do it. Well, it would all be settled properly in a few weeks. Reverend Mother de Murinais had at last given the date of her return. The house was now filling with the nuns who had left ten years before. There were a few children to teach in the school. In Holy Week, Fr Rivet gathered together a number of people for a retreat in the convent chapel. Life was coming back. Even though Reverend Mother de Murinais was in her eightieth year, she was coming back. Philippine prepared her room with care.

"Why are you getting this other room ready near our superior's?" asked Mother la Fontaine. "It's a much better one than poor Mother Lalanne has."

"It's for Mother Cousin," said Philippine. "She says she is coming back to be able to look after the health of Reverend Mother. That is to be her employment."

Mother la Fontaine raised her eyebrows.

"Why, she's quite young. What right has she to specify what she is to do? And to have one of the best rooms? But I suppose that's your arrangement. You young people!"

"Well," said Philippine, "you can't say that about the other two lay-sisters Reverend Mother is bringing with her—one's over eighty."

"Ridiculous!" said Mother la Fontaine. "What help can she be in a half-ruined house like this?"

At last the carriage wheels were heard turning in through the gateway. The travellers climbed out. Philippine was surprised to see how bent and feeble Reverend Mother de Murinais had grown. She took her arm and led her in. She was tired, and wanted only to rest. Philippine found herself shooed out of the way by the young companion. It did not matter. This was the day she had waited for. To-morrow was Holy Thursday. They would all be reunited in their cenacle.

"We'll open the exterior door to-day," she said the next morning. "It's time we showed the world that it can come into church openly again."

Mother Faucherand shrugged her shoulders, but the door that had been so many years shut swung back on its hinges. The bell rang for the office. Philippine was waiting by the door of the choir. Reverend Mother de Murinais came slowly along the corridor. Her novice daughter ran forward and took her by the arm. With a heart beating high with triumphant joy, she led her to her stall. Then she took her place on the lowest seat. Her work was over. Ste Marie's was Ste Marie's again.

"We don't need to alter our dress, do we, Reverend Mother?" asked Mother Cousin later in the year. "Sister Duchesne appears to think we all should look the same. I don't know that it matters to her, does it? I don't think you at any rate should change what you've been used to wearing."

Mother de Murinais sighed. Since her return two months ago, this kind of remark had been made to her every other day. If only her daughters would live peacefully together! Sister Duchesne seemed to have a genius for rubbing them up the wrong way. Why must she show that she did not approve of some of the things they did or did not do? She must know that the health of some did not allow of fasting, that some must go to bed earlier than the time of rule, that it wasn't a mortal sin not to have reading in the refectory. It was obviously very difficult, when you had been out in the world so long, to return to religious silence. There was probably not much harm in saying a word to a friend whenever you wanted to—at least it was a form of charity that outweighed the sourness of censorious criticism. In time, perhaps, she would be able to get her daughters to conform more nearly to the rule. But at the moment she must go gently. Some of them had undoubtedly understood that they were just being offered a shelter for their old age. She would let things go on. That was the only way to have peace and quiet.

In the chapel Philippine was weeping. It was 2 July, the special Feast of the Visitation and she was alone with her Lord. All that had passed in the last months rose to her mind. Was not the Sacred Heart mourning as when He spoke to Sister Margaret Mary, reproaching men for their coldness and contempt for Him in His adorable sacrament of love, and showing the deep wound that those consecrated to His service made by their infidelity. Was this lukewarm, mitigated observance all that He had a right to expect after the outrages of the Revolution? How should the horrors of the past be atoned for if love had grown so cold in His own sanctuary? Was she the obstacle to the good to be done in His house? Did He ask of her the sacrifice of leaving? Bitterness surged through her heart and she prayed, "O my Lord, must it be that on this very Feast of the Visitation I should have to separate myself from the order which bears its name?" A warm stream filled her mouth and she raised her handkerchief. It was covered with blood. She had broken a blood vessel in her anguish, and now even she must leave the chapel, she who had wanted to be the one faithful spouse when all others had deserted Him.

That evening Fr Rivet came to the convent. He saw Philippine and stopped her in a corridor.

"My child, what is the matter? You look pale and ill."

"I've been weeping," she told him simply.

He had eyes to see and knew the reason for her tears. He shook his head.

"You have not wept enough, yet, my child. This is only the

beginning of your sorrows. You must arm yourself with courage."

What else could he say to her? The situation was dark and uncertain.

"If it's the labour that frightens them," Philippine thought as she tried to find what needed to be done, "I will do it. Perhaps it was my fault in wanting to hurry things too much. Well, I will do the work in the sacristy and be portress too. I can manage to do the buying of supplies and take care of the younger children. That may tide things over—when the building gets more like its old self, perhaps then they will be more like their old selves. I could put up with anything if only Reverend Mother would make them keep the rule."

For a week or more she struggled on. She felt that more and more the nuns were slighting her. Did that matter? Was it self-love that made her grieve? She knew that she was free from self-seeking and, in the light of that knowledge, went to Reverend Mother de Murinais.

The old superior was sitting in a low chair at her desk, reading quietly. She looked up as Philippine opened the door and shut it quickly. In another moment, the youngest of her daughters was at her feet, the tears pouring down her face.

"Dear, dear," said Reverend Mother de Murinais, twisting round in distress. "What on earth's the matter? I can't stand scenes, Sister Duchesne. Please tell me quietly what is wrong."

"Can't you see?" cried Philippine. "Everything's wrong. Where is our Holy Rule? What would St Jane de Chantal say if she saw us? What is Our Lord thinking of our half-hearted service?"

"Pull yourself together, Sister," said Reverend Mother de Murinais. "You are getting yourself into a state of hysteria. There's nothing so very wrong with the house. In time you'll see that your view is exaggerated. Give your sisters time to make their adjustment to religious life again."

"They've had time," said Philippine. "Can't you see that things are going from bad to worse? I implore you, for the love

H

of God, take in hand the government of this house firmly and insist upon strict observance."

Reverend Mother de Murinais rose to her feet and rang her little bell. In a moment Mother Cousin had entered.

"That will do, Sister Duchesne," said the superior. "Take things more quietly. Mother Cousin, will you give me your arm to the garden?"

Philippine went away. She had nothing more to say. Courage? She must weep still more.

The twenty-first of August was the feast of St Jane de Chantal. Philippine was on her way to the chapel to prepare for the High Mass. In the corridor by her superior's room a nun was bending over some bundles, strapping their contents.

"Can I help?" Philippine asked, then paused, surprised. "What are you packing up, Mother—?"

Mother Cousin rose to her feet.

"Nothing of yours, Sister Duchesne. These are just things we brought with us. We are leaving on the twenty-fifth."

Philippine went to the chapel feeling stunned.

"Let me go if I am the obstacle to good being done here," she prayed. "It is Your Will, not mine, that I want done. Let me go rather than that You should be abandoned."

But no answer came then to her prayer. The other nuns busied themselves with preparations for leaving. On the eve of 25 August, Mother Cousin came to Philippine.

"Reverend Mother wants to see you," she said.

In her room, the old superior was calmly sitting in her chair, a smile on her wrinkled face.

"Come in, Sister Duchesne," she said, and as Philippine knelt beside her, she added kindly, "I want to tell you that we shall be leaving to-morrow morning."

Philippine burst into tears. This then was the end. Irrevocable. Or was there hope—when things in France were more settled? When things within the house were better provided for? Must she really give up all hope?

"Reverend Mother," she said, "can I not hope that you will come back?"

There was no regret in Reverend Mother de Murinais's voice as she replied: "No, my dear sister, I shall never come back. That is quite impossible. I am too old for new undertakings. Too old. At eighty, my dear sister, there is need for rest and quiet. New undertakings are for the young. New undertakings require courage. No, I shall not come back."

It was the end. Philippine rose and went out.

Next morning as Paul was coming up the hill from Grenoble on his way to work, he caught sight of the roof of Ste Marie's, cold grey in the early sunlight. It looked grim, he thought, like a prison. What a pity Mlle Duchesne was locked up in it! She was a one for telling stories! He remembered them as well as if he had heard them yesterday. The best one was the one about Fr de Brébœuf and all the tortures of the Indians. Paul was level now with the archway that led up to the convent. He had to jump in to the side of the road to avoid the wheels of a carriage that was setting off down the hill. It seemed full of ladies in black, and there were some more coming out through the doorway at the top. He wondered vaguely what they were doing, then set off again up the hill, with his thoughts on Fr de Brébœuf. Mlle Duchesne had said that at the end he had cried out, "Bear with courage these few remaining tortures—" then they had cut open his breast while he was still alive and torn his heart out. Paul wondered if it hurt him terrifically.

Within Ste Marie's, Philippine was weeping bitterly.

In Paris Napoleon Bonaparte was just congratulating himself on having been made First Consul for life at the age of thirty-three.

14: On the Edge of the Glacier

Tongues were wagging in Grenoble. Now that Mlle Duchesne had failed completely, a great number of people openly affirmed that they had known all along that it was a hairbrained scheme doomed from the very start.

"We might have realized," said Henriette de Saussure, embroidering by the open windows while her husband read beside her, "that Philippine's uncompromising character was not the one to succeed as a leader. No one could get on easily with her if she had her own idea about things."

"Remarkable insight you have, my dear," said Frédéric, laying his book on his knees. "But I, too, have insight into character—female character to boot."

"I suppose," Henriette retorted, "that you mean that the other nuns, being women, could be imperfect—"

"Petty, at any rate," said Frédéric. "Well, what else did you pick up this morning?"

"I met Mme de Mauduit—with Mélanie. She says that M. Duchesne is coming back from Paris to settle down here."

"He's giving up his political career?" asked Frédéric in surprise. His wife nodded.

"Mme de Mauduit says he won't stand Bonaparte's latest honour—says it's the death of true democracy—another form of tyranny—new name, old spirit. She said that perhaps this would bring Philippine to her senses, and that she would settle down with him reasonably. I thought so, too, but Mélanie contradicted her sister outright."

"Another chip off the old block," commented Frédéric with a smile. "She must be about sixteen now—with an opinion of her own."

"Mélanie told me that the Visitation at Romans was re-opening. Their cousin Marie Tranchant is returning. I should think the best thing Philippine could do would be to go there. She must see now that she has failed, Duchesne or no Duchesne. She seems to have made a mess of the whole of her life. She was really gifted at school, and she's done nothing, whereas I—"

"Have managed to marry me," said Frédéric.

Henriette shook her brown curls.

"Do be serious, Frédéric. You might have some influence with her—she would respect your mind. You might make her see the folly of going on."

"I might," said Frédéric, getting up and looking out of the window. "But I wouldn't try."

"Why? Don't you think she is stupidly obstinate over this matter of Ste Marie's? What do you think, Frédéric?"

"I think she's gloriously wrong-headed—"

"There! Then persuade her to come home."

"Let me finish, my dear. Wrong in the head, but completely right in the heart."

"What do you mean?"

Her husband was looking across the valley. He answered with his eyes on the chain of mountains.

"I mean she has the artist's instinct to see the correct thing to do without being able to give a full reason for doing it. I have it sometimes when I make poetry—she has it when she is making her life. There's a marvellous view of the peaks from here, Henriette."

"Frédéric, we're not discussing the view," said Henriette, pouting.

"It's Mlle Duchesne's view," said her husband softly. "Listen, my dear. When I was a boy, my father had a little chalet near Chamonix where we used to spend the summer months... Wherever we scrambled round about it, we could see the great gleaming dome of Mont Blanc. It fascinated me. I used to sit and watch the play of cloud and sunlight on its snows and glaciers, and nearly weep for the beauty of it—I even made up a poem about it. Let me see—yes:

> Bright beauty unattainable,
> Pure snows no man can sear,
> Serene in glacial solitude,
> We mortals gaze and fear——"

"I don't know what your juvenile effusions have to do with the point we are debating," said Henriette, pursuing her embroidery.

"Wait," said Frédéric. "There was another boy living in Chamonix at the same time, a grubby, scrubby son of a mountaineer. Jacques Balmat used to climb to the very same places I knew of and watch Mont Blanc, but he did not expend himself in—juvenile effusions. In his heart grew the resolution to reach that unattained summit, to tread those snows no human foot had touched, and when companions laughed at him, he shut up his thoughts within his own heart, and went off on solitary climbs, always seeking a way that would lead him to the heights. Through boyhood he grew to manhood, and still the way had not been found—always a barrier of rock or glacier had cut short his attempts. Then one day, it seemed, luck was with him. At last the route was clear. Higher and higher he found the way opening before him as the sun reached its zenith and began to decline. It was a race against time but hope climbed with him. Then the last rays of light showed him a great tongue of glacier that barred his path."

"Go on," said Henriette, her needle stuck in her work.

"Common sense said, 'Jacques Balmat, you are done for again this time. Go back while it is still light enough to see the descent. Mont Blanc is unscalable. If you stay here, you will be just one more of the victims the mountain has claimed.' 'Good', answered Jacques Balmat. 'There is much reason in what you say, and I should have time to get back to a hot helping of onion stew in the goatherd's hut.' Then he slipped off his rucksack and placed it firmly on a ledge of the ice, settled himself on it, pulling his coat round about him, and waited where he was through the long black night, fighting the sleep that lay in wait for him hand in hand with death. And in the morning—"

"What happened in the morning?" Henriette asked quickly as he stopped.

"In the morning the sun shone down across the glacier and the last part of the route to the summit was made clear."

"And he reached the top?" Henriette asked again.

"Not that day, my dear," said Frédéric with his eyes still on the peaks. "The way had been seen but there were practical difficulties to be coped with. He waited, knowing he was right, and then when all was ready, he climbed the mountain."

"Alone?"

"No, he took some companions with him, men who at last believed in him."

"What a good thing he did not turn back that night on the glacier!" said Henriette.

"You see that, do you?" her husband said. "Don't you see it, too, for Mlle Duchesne?"

"You mean she is climbing a mountain?"

"If I believed like you, Henriette, I should call it the mountain of God. But as I am only a poet, an artist, I can only see what she is doing as a work of art, a form of creation. I recognize the artist in others. Some, like me, write about life, some, like Mlle Duchesne, live it. I express ideas with my mouth, she with her whole being. The creator must complete his work of art—poem, symphony, life, what you will. There is something inartistic in turning back. It is a work not rounded off."

"But what if your Jacques Balmat had frozen to death?" asked his wife, frowning.

"Does it matter?" asked Frédéric. "He would have completed his work of art as truly as if he had reached the summit. There is a beauty about undefeated failure."

"So you mean her work of art will be holiness?" said Henriette, looking out on the mountains whose peaks were gleaming now in the August sun.

"Nothing less will content her," answered Frédéric.

"You are queer, Frédéric," said Henriette. "If you see that, why do you not follow in her steps?"

He shrugged his shoulders.

"The will, my dear, is lacking. Faith should move that. An unbeliever must be excused if he simply sits on the greensward in the valley and admires the view. I leave it to you to climb the mountain of God after her. You are a Christian to whom it has been said, 'Be ye perfect'."

"That's a hard saying, Frédéric. It's not so easy to know how to be a saint."

"Perhaps that is the reason for artists in all forms of creation. They go ahead and show the way."

"You may be right," said Henriette. "All the same, until the artist in sanctity is a saint, she's dreadfully hard to live with."

At the presbytery, Fr Rivet was speaking to his sister before taking his evening walk.

"I am going up to Ste Marie d'en Haut," he said.

"I'm glad," answered his sister. "They're saying cruel things about Mlle Duchesne. When they saw Reverend Mother de Murinais and her companions go off this morning they said it proved that no one could live with her. For two pins I'd go off and join her, just to prove them wrong."

"I heard from Fr Roger to-day," said Fr Rivet, reflectively.

"The one who belongs to the Fathers of the Faith?" asked his sister. "They are a valiant set of men. I wonder how long they will have to wait until they can become Jesuits again."

She was wondering, too, how long it would be before she

could become a Carmelite again. Her brother looked at her.

"Pray," he said enigmatically and went off.

Philippine was not wasting her time in idle weeping. There was one lay helper who had not deserted the monastery and together they coped with all the work. The seven young children were already in bed when the priest arrived. Only seventeen-year-old Emilie Giraud was still up. Philippine was able to see Fr Rivet when he rang the doorbell. They went out on to the terrace while he spoke to her with pitying kindness. God was still in His heaven. The town at their feet could fret and plan and counter-plan. The great chain of mountains were not more stable than God's faithful care.

"He is Lord of Life," the priest said. "Life springs up even at the snow line, doesn't it? I was hearing of fresh life to-day. Fr Roger wrote to me of a new little institute that is being formed by his friend Fr Varin—at least, that is the wrong way to put it. It is growing up with a life that comes straight from the Sacred Heart. Fr Varin only watches over it."

"From the Sacred Heart?" cried Philippine. The priest smiled.

"Of course that attracts you, my child, and you would like its rules, too, since they are adapted from those of St Ignatius. The nuns have opened a school for girls in Amiens. They want to glorify Our Lord's Sacred Heart by training women to know and love Him and to re-establish religion in France."

Philippine was looking at him intently, as he went on.

"They teach rich and poor. They want to win the whole world to Our Lord. France will not be big enough for their Mother Superior's heart. Prayer is the source of their strength —Fr Roger tells me they must be Carmelites for prayers and Sisters of Charity for devotedness."

"What are you telling me this for?" asked Philippine, though she knew already what his answer would be.

"Because Ste Marie's has been left desolate—because you are weeping like the Holy Women at an empty tomb—and because God is God of the living—"

"And because you are the Angel of the Resurrection to give me glad tidings," cried Philippine. "You come to tell me of a resurrection that God proposes."

"Yes," said the priest. "Shall I write to Fr Roger to tell him that Ste Marie's is now unoccupied, and that you would welcome help from the founder of the Amiens congregation, if she would send some nuns here?"

Philippine was silent. The setting sun was throwing the shadows of the mountains over the hill of Rabot, and filling the valley with purple dusk. It was close upon night, and darkness would soon shroud everything. But darkness was now friendly. There had to be darkness before dawn. At dawn, a ray would strike across from behind the highest distant peaks and light even the coldest of glaciers. She faced Fr Rivet with a smile of happiness.

"Please write," she said. Was not her heart burning as he talked to her in the way?

15: *The Height of Ambition*

ON All Saints' day, Mme Rivet came to live at Ste Marie's. In her wise maturity she recognized the work of God in Philippine Duchesne. Young, unspoiled Emilie Giraud sensed the same thing and asked to be allowed to go from school to the community. Worthy Mlle Balastron joined them.

"You must be superior," Philippine said to Fr Rivet's sister. "The Vicar General has promised to give us a working rule. We'll want some sort of name, too."

"Daughters of the Propagation of the Faith" seemed to express their desires, and simple vows of chastity and obedience satisfied them while they waited. There was work to do, for the school now numbered eighteen. Work seemed good when they were preparing the way for a great opportunity.

"Thank God a thousand times," said Philippine, "for having given us this task of getting things ready for those who will come here to receive the Word of God and carry it to distant lands. We'll be even happier if we are allowed to enter this holy new society. I'm not a bit worthy of it, so that it will be pure mercy if they take me. We'll be all trying then to rescue souls to give them to our great Master."

"Yes, but when will that be?" asked the new postulant, Mlle Second.

"Please God, soon," said Mother Rivet. "We're expecting

Fr Roger to come here with Fr Varin next week, on the Feast of St Ignatius.''

"Fr Varin!" exclaimed Emilie Giraud. "I shall be afraid of him—he used to be a soldier and I'm sure he'll be fierce."

"It's he who has been helping Mother Barat," said Philippine. "I don't suppose he will think us as holy as she is, and that's the only real thing that matters."

"Then we must pray that his eyes are held," Mlle Balastron suggested. But to Philippine, it was no subject for joking.

The two Fathers of the Faith arrived in time for Mass. They treated the sacristan with courteous silence, and when the Holy Sacrifice had been offered, went with few words to the parlour for their breakfast.

"I've not had a word from them," said Philippine, waiting outside with Mother Rivet. "You'll have to do the talking when they go over the house, as you are the superior. But may I follow, too?"

"Of course," said Mother Rivet. "I doubt if we shall know what they are thinking. Such mortified men have iron control over their feelings."

The two fathers began the rounds. They stopped with interest at the grille.

"Yes," remarked Fr Varin, glancing at Philippine from under his eyebrows. "This will do very well for the Visitation."

She did not answer him. With his experienced eyes upon her, how could she say that she thought God did not now want her for the Visitation?

They examined everything, noting the size and position of rooms, seeing the unrepaired damage of the years of dereliction. They asked questions. They made no statements. By the end of the day Philippine was no wiser.

"They mean to go after breakfast to-morrow morning," said Mother Rivet. "We'll see them then. Perhaps by that time they will thaw. If only they would give a hint!"

But the next morning the two fathers seemed as impenetrable. Mother Rivet steered the conversation towards the point at issue. Fr Varin turned in his chair and faced Philippine.

"Those who would work for God must cultivate holy indifference," he said. "What does it matter where we are or what we do, provided we are where God wishes us to be and doing what He wishes us to do? You believe that?"

"Yes," said Philippine quickly, "but—"

"Good," Fr Varin went on, ignoring her further thought. "God's ways are wonderful. Think of the time those mountains out yonder took in the making. Think of the years that passed before the fullness of time saw the coming of Our Lord. Think of the slowness of preparation, the care and waiting that go to the accomplishment of any of His works."

Mother Rivet's heart sank. So they had not satisfied the two fathers. They would have to wait still longer. But Philippine was on her feet.

"Why, Father," she cried, all awe of the priest swept away in her eagerness for what she had set her heart upon, "if St Francis Xavier had so argued the pros and cons of a thing, before doing God's work, he'd not have got so much done in ten years."

Mother Rivet gasped at such temerity, but the two fathers broke into smiles.

"All right," said Fr Varin, rising. "I promise you that Mother Barat will come."

It was clear that his words had let loose a joy that was not wholly of this world.

"I am right," thought the holy priest. "I came here prejudiced. My better judgement said, 'Don't start another house before the first one at Amiens is firmly established. Above all, don't start it with novices who are old and set in their ways.' But I knew for certain last night at Benediction that I was wrong—that I was using only human wisdom. I must get back and see Sophie Barat as soon as I can, and tell her that there are companions here who will be a help to her, especially one. If there were only Philippine Duchesne, why, she would be worth seeking at the ends of the world."

In the weeks that followed, Emilie Giraud was a little uncertain.

"How shall I get on with this Mother Barat?" she wondered. "They say she comes from Joigny in Burgundy—that might mean anything. It's not an important town and she is only a wine-cooper's daughter. But then she's dreadfully learned, and very clever, and she's founded an order, so I suppose she's got a strong character and will be imposing. But then they say she's only twenty-five. She's much too young for Mother Duchesne to have to obey. I don't think I shall like it at all if I see her as superior here. It was Mother Duchesne who taught me to love God and souls. I suppose I shan't be able to talk to her again about the missions and going out to Japan like St Francis Xavier. Things won't be a bit the same. But she's looking forward to it, so perhaps it will be possible to get on with Mother Barat. But she's only six years older than me. I can't imagine how she can have got holy enough to be a superior in the time."

Philippine counted the days through September, October, November. Towards the end of the month a letter dated 2 November arrived from Mother Barat. She read it to the others and their hearts warmed.

"Listen to this," she said. " 'I am filled with joy at seeing your souls so well disposed and therefore so ready to fulfil the designs of our loving God. I am deeply sorry that Our Lord has looked upon me and chosen me to cultivate your good dispositions—so many other persons would have done it so much better than I, and I should not dare to do so, were it not that I trust wholly in God. But plants that are grown in a good fertile soil do not want much skill or care on the part of the gardener. I expect that is why Our Lord has chosen a poor wretched creature like me... It is so consoling for me to find souls who want to love God and to make Him loved, and are ready to sacrifice everything for His glory... How I long to see you!... I shall leave Amiens on the twenty-second... soon we shall be one together, so we must already be united in Our Lord.' She signs herself 'Your very humble servant, Sophie Barat.' She must be on her way now. She is bringing two companions, a young choir nun and a sister. We must get ready for them.''

The same day that Mother Barat wrote her letter, another traveller set out on a journey to bring peace. Pius VII left Rome and passed through Italy and France on his way to Paris. The way was hard in the winter weather for him, though special coach arrangements were made, for he came by a personal invitation from the Corsican who swayed the destinies of the eldest daughter of the Church. Slower and more difficult were the means of travel that Mother Barat had to take so that she was still on the road when he had reached Paris on 28 November. Four days later, he went through the age-long form of the consecration of one who accepts temporal power for the protection of the members of God's Church. Colour and lights made gorgeous the grey walls of Notre Dame as prayer succeeded prayer, but when the moment came for the coronation, Napoleon Bonaparte rose from his knees and himself took the crown from the altar and placed it on his own head. Emperor of France, supreme, unquestioned. At thirty-three, he held the future in his hands.

"To-day Mother Barat will be here," said Philippine on the morning of 13 December. They had everything ready to welcome the travellers long before the earliest hour they could arrive. Emilie Giraud wandered up and down the corridor by the cloister. Mother Rivet sat calmly saying her beads with her eyes closed. Mlle Balastron and Mlle Second tried to pray while their ears were pricked to catch the least sound in the road outside. Philippine stood at the top end of the passage that led to the door. How dark and gloomy and dank it seemed in the fading light of the December day! Then there came a knock at the outer door. It was opened by the portress and the watching group saw a small frail young woman framed against the evening sky. They saw her eyes alight with joy and hands held out in greeting. Like a whirlwind, Philippine was down the corridor and on her knees. Beside herself with happiness, she

Like a whirlwind, Philippine was down the corridor and on her knees.

kissed the feet of Mother Barat as she cried out, "At last I see upon the mountain the feet of those who come to give us tidings of peace and true good!" This was the day of the joy of her heart. Now she would be able to sink into the background and only live to serve others and obey. Thirty-three years had been a long time to wait.

16: Sunlight

"THINGS are much better than I could ever have imagined," Emilie Giraud told herself, as she walked in the garden saying her midday prayers, while the snow sparkled in the sunlight and the crisp cold made her tingle with energy. "How good Mother Barat is to each one of us! Look at the time she's given to me and I'm the youngest of all. And the things she has said to me—'Spring is the time to cultivate young plants especially when they are ready to let the gardener do what he wants. What a nice surprise when we find you with leaves and perhaps with flowers! But you don't need me to make you grow. I'm nothing and less than nothing. The Master of all is the true Gardener who does everything. Listen to Him, love Him, burn with desire for Him.' Well, that's what she does herself. Last night when we sat up waiting for the Christmas Office and the Midnight Mass, it was like being in Bethlehem to hear her speak of Our Lord—'God submitting Himself to two of His creatures—how could any of us cling to self-love after seeing that? Ah, if only people knew how over-whelmingly lovable He is in the arms of His Mother—how already His little Heart is burning with love for us. Make Him known, my dear daughters, and soon He will be loved; above all, make Him known to those foolish pious folk who put limits to the mercy of our God.' Those words of hers made my heart feel bigger—I think she's pushed out of it a whole lot of

things that were making me afraid. I wonder what she thinks
of Mother Duchesne? I know she loves her. I saw that right
from the first moment they looked at each other. I suppose
that's what people mean by love at first sight. But she can't say
to her that there aren't yet leaves and flowers on her plant. I
should think she sees that there's a pretty good strong tree
there. But perhaps it's like the trees this Christmas morning,
all covered with snow, and then people can't see them
properly."

Emilie stopped and watched the sunlight play upon the
burden of snow upheld by one of the garden trees. Clear in the
blue sky the sun shone warmly. Little prisms on the white
mantle broke up into rainbow colours, diamond bright. On
the upper branches, the snow began melting, shifted slowly,
then with a rush, flaked off, while the boughs sprang upward,
released from the weight.

"How strong and lovely the tree looks now against the
blue sky!" Emilie thought. "Mother Barat told me to say my
prayers out here and to thank God for all I saw. That's one
thing to be grateful for—and another is the view of the mountains. When you see their peaks gleaming in the brightness of a
day like this, it makes you want to be a mountaineer. What was
it Mother Duchesne said? 'How beautiful upon the mountains
are the feet of those who come to give us tidings of peace and
true good!' That means Mother Barat's—but it's queer—
those are the words used when you say goodbye to missionaries. Missionaries! And we're going to be enclosed nuns. Ah,
well."

"Be at peace," the young new superior told Philippine, "I
only want your good. All that I am, all that I have is yours.
Trust God. Don't think that you have great new sacrifices to
make—no, it's just giving up your self-will in little things, trying to get a spirit of humility and gentleness, and the spirit of
prayer. You say you want the cross. I think God has reserved a
large portion for you, but have courage. You know that it's the
greatest of treasures. Don't ask for crosses but accept them

wholeheartedly when they come. Just soak yourself through
and through with the love of Jesus."

"And when can we begin our noviciate?" asked Philippine.

"On the last day of the year," answered Mother Barat.

"The last day of the year!" cried Philippine. "The first day
of our new birth to this life we have chosen!"

Gently but firmly Mother Barat showed them what they
should do. They learnt from her own way of acting what their
spirit should be. Generous, self-effacing, looking always to
Jesus Christ's Heart as their model, they began to find lighthearted happiness in their labours and Mother Barat's wit set
them laughing gaily at recreations. Philippine found again a
fund of fun she thought she had outgrown. Then in February,
Fr Roger of the Fathers of the Faith arrived to give them a retreat.

"You've a daughter who is very austere," he said to Mother
Barat, "and she will need the brake and not the rein. We must
make her understand self-renouncement thoroughly—and the
others who have lived with her, too."

"I think you will find they are ready—" began Mother
Barat.

"Self-will creeps in everywhere," said the priest with
finality. "I shall wage a war to the death. First, the instructions
will be given not in the chapel where they may grow sentimental over all the pious associations with the past, but in the
little room over the top end of the church. I have permission
from the bishop to say Mass there and to reserve the Blessed
Sacrament, so they'll not need to go to the chapel at all."

"And office, Father?" asked Mother Barat.

"Upstairs too," he said.

Mother Rivet met him later and pointed out that seculars
came in to hear office. There would perhaps be scandal if there
was none. He looked at her sternly.

"Mother Debrosse who has come from Amiens will not be
making this retreat. There are children in the school. She can
train them to say office in your stead."

That was the last objection. The new novices submitted to having the already small room halved by a linen curtain. Dutifully they all five sat on the one bench in front. Intently they listened to his words, stern, direct, cutting down to the bone. As his instructions progressed, the mountain of religious life grew steeper and steeper, the flowers thinned by the wayside, the grass withered, and the bare rock remained. He spoke of poverty.

"You must own nothing, my dear sisters, nothing. You must want nothing, nothing. You must prefer nothing. Nothing. Nothing."

Emilie Giraud stirred uneasily on the bench. Mother Duchesne took alarm. This austere talk might scare away her young companions.

"This is to try us," she whispered to them.

Next time he spoke of obedience.

"You must do the will of those who hold the place of God," he said. "You must give up your own will, your own way of working, your own way of deciding, your own way of planning, your own way of feeling."

Adelaide Second shifted in her place. Anxiously Mother Duchesne glanced at her.

"This is to try us," she whispered once more.

Again Fr Roger showed them the need of humility.

"What are you in fact, my dear sisters?" he asked. "Dust mixed with a bit of water—mud, slime. And you think yourself someone? I tell you, you are no one. Who should treat you with any consideration? I tell you again, you are nothing, nothing, and only fit to be trodden underfoot."

There was a general movement along the bench. Again Philippine leant forward.

"This is to try us," she whispered with increased trepidation. Would the prospect prove too grim for them to face?

The priest pursued his theme.

"What have you entered for? To work for God—He the Creator, you the mere creature—and you expect to have a return for your services? A pat on the back? To swim in consolations in prayer? I tell you, my dear sisters, when every minute of the day and night is filled for God alone, when you are worn out with your labours and the butt of harsh criticism, when your times of prayer are as arid as the Sahara, you can turn to Him and say, 'We are unprofitable servants.'"

"This is to try us," Philippine countered in an agitated whisper.

Mother Rivet buried her head in her hands. Mother Balastron's shoulders shook and shook. Mother Second put her handkerchief to her mouth to stop strange squeaks and gurgles. Mother Giraud gave way completely and ripples of laughter broke into the instruction. Unaware of the whispered commentary on his words, the priest looked at the row of his exercitants still shaking with emotion.

"Worn-out or pent-up nerves," he thought, then aloud he said, "I see you need some relaxation. You will have recreation each day—and I will preside."

At the very first, the conversation turned to fasting. Fr Roger asked Philippine, "Have you been accustomed to fast?"

"Oh, yes, Father," she answered. "It's penance for my sins, and a way of gaining graces for others. I wouldn't be without the opportunity for anything."

"H'm. And how often do you keep these fast days?"

"At least once a week, Father."

The priest said nothing. But at the evening instruction he announced, "To-morrow all will fast and have dry bread for supper. All except Mother Duchesne."

The next day, the four went breakfastless to their cells. When Philippine entered hers, her eyes lit on a plate piled high with many kinds of fruit. Beside it was a large piece of bread and a cup of steaming coffee. A note lay folded on the plate. "Take all of this," she read. "It won't hurt you."

The next recreation conversation turned to the reciting of office in choir.

"Mother Duchesne kept us all to it even when we were only

four and had the school to look after as well," said Emilie Giraud proudly.

"Good," said Fr Roger. "Now you will say office no more."

Obediently they accepted his decision, grieved that they must sacrifice the time of praising God, but convinced that obedience was better. How should they guess that he said it again only to try them?

"To-morrow," he told them, "you will take to Mother Barat the thing to which you cling most."

Nothing appeared on the morrow. He took them to task.

"But, Father," said Philippine, bold in desperation, "when you give orders, you ought to make them possible. I can't take to Reverend Mother this house and everything in it—and that's all I care about on earth."

The retreat drew to a close. One more thing Fr Roger demanded of them. "To-day is Saturday," he reminded them. "It's a day set apart for the special honouring of Our Lady. None of you will say her beads to-day." And none of them did. Fr Roger went in jubilation to Mother Barat.

"You have the material of saints there," he told her. "They are docile to the Will of God in small things and in great. God will do great things with them. I have been privileged to speak with them. One does not give two such retreats in a lifetime."

When he had gone and work was resumed, they were glad to listen once more to their new Mother.

"That's the most extraordinary and rigorous retreat I've ever made," said Mother Rivet. "Are all the Fathers of the Faith so austere?"

"My brother is one," said Mother Barat with a smile.

"Now that it's over," said Mother Balastron, "I feel that it was like going for a long walk through the snow—it's perishingly cold at the time, but when you're indoors again, you tingle with warmth and vigour."

"It all sounded pretty grim," Mother Second reflected.

"It isn't," said Mother Barat, "once you've decided to become little, and simple, and mortified, willing to be nothing

either in the order of nature or even in the order of grace, if
God wants it so."

"There are so many things I want to do for Him," sighed
Philippine.

"Yes," Mother Barat answered her, "but to please Jesus,
only one thing is needed—just wanting to love Him and do
His Will."

"It sounded dreadfully difficult to become a saint," Mother
Giraud said.

"Don't think of the difficulties," Mother Barat encouraged
her youngest daughter. "Just love God and live only to please
Him, and you'll soon be swimming in an ocean of happiness.
You'll find all the help you need in His Heart."

Philippine discovered the truth of her words. New postulants arrived, the school grew, calumnies launched against the
young superior and the new institute were calmly lived down.
Mother Deshayes joined them from Amiens with all her vigorous forthrightness. Fr Varin came to preach courage and confidence. Fr Barat, too, arrived.

"I want you to meet my brother," said Mother Barat, and
Mother Duchesne obeyed with some fear. Had he not a repu-
tation for learning before which her knowledge was nothing?
And did they not also say that his virtues were those of a saint?
He was waiting for her in the parlour and turned to greet her.
In silence their eyes met and they understood each other. There
was no need for small talk between two souls who longed to
spread the knowledge of God.

"The devil is more eager and persevering in trying to de-
stroy souls than we are to save them," he said.

"Well, Father, what can we do to gain souls? Isn't it prayer
and penance that we must give?"

"I think so," he said. "Look at the power that so many
saints have gained by being always ready to be sacrificed. We
must be strong souls, Mother, we who want to imitate our
great Model. The true lover of Jesus must let the keen sword of
loving sorrow pierce his heart, sorrow for the loss of souls. And

then we want to do penance and make our life a life of prayer."

When 21 November came round, the novices were allowed to take their first vows. Fr Varin was there at the Mass and preached on the text, "This day will be famous among you." Before the Blessed Sacrament exposed, they knelt, with Mother Barat standing to the right of the altar. A famous day? Philippine's eyes could not look into a future that would see here two saints side by side where once St Francis of Sales and St Jane de Chantal had been. To her this was the day of her long-deferred desire. The novice of nearly twenty years was at last the spouse of Christ. Nothing could part them now.

M. Duchesne climbed the hill some days later to see his daughter. He was beginning to stoop a little but his eyes were as keen and his observation as vigorous as of old.

"They've not made you Reverend Mother," he remarked with a smile that his daughter understood. "Is it true that Mother Barat is returning to Amiens?"

"Yes," said Philippine. "It's a great sacrifice for us all, but Mother Deshayes takes her place."

"Your sisters are thinking of sending their children to school here," M. Duchesne said. "I shall support their intention. It seems to me that things are well run."

As he walked down the hill again, one thought filled his mind.

"Philippine is somehow right—like a hand in a well-fitting glove. No mistaking it to-day—she's happy."

A few days later, on 2 December 1805, Napoleon was jubilating over the defeat of the Allies at Austerlitz.

17: *Starlight*

As a Trappist monk, Dom Augustine de Lestrange had the greatest faith in prayer. Only Revolution and war had made him and his brethren move from La Trappe to Switzerland, from Switzerland to Russia, to Germany, to Poland, to Denmark, and finally to America. Now that he was back again in France, he welcomed the opportunity of speaking on this Feast of the Epiphany, 1806, to the nuns who kept the school at Ste Marie d'en Haut, for they would then pray for the souls he had met like sheep without a shepherd.

"I have been to Louisiana," he told them. "Now, alas, no longer French. Napoleon could have had it back. He found it more profitable to let the United States buy it. Our French people are being submerged now, and their faith with them. I have been up and down the valleys of the Mississippi and the Missouri, and everywhere there are ruined churches and people without pastors. A country of breathtaking beauty lies there, and God its Creator is not known. Yet here and there among Indians sunk in paganism I have found lingering the faith planted by the heroic Jesuits of former days, and the cry goes up from their hearts, 'Give us again priests.' My dear sisters, though all the work you do is here in France, teaching French children, by your prayers you can visit those other souls. By your prayers you can help to bring light to those who sit in the outer darkness. God's time seems ripe. A great and free nation holds the destinies of thousands and thousands of men and women who are reaching out to the lands ever more westward. Your prayers will be all-powerful over the heart of Our Lord. In this octave of the Epiphany, you will remember those who are still looking for the star."

Four days later, Mother Duchesne was on her knees in the children's dormitory, making her early morning meditation in the dark. From the white-curtained cubicles came the regular breathing of sleeping children and the creaking of a bed here and there as a coverlet was drawn more snugly over shoulders that felt the keen nip of the unwarmed room. A draught like a knife edge cut under the heavy wooden door. All night the large flakes of snow had drifted down, but now the sky was clear and black over a white world and from the narrow window, made narrower by its framework of thick snow, Philippine could see a single star shining above the convent chapel. The star had come to rest. The Mother and the Child were there again at last, in her own beloved Ste Marie d'en Haut. How good God was! Good to have brought together by His guiding star a band of faithful servants, good to let the praise of His Son's Sacred Heart be heard here again, good to have given them these souls of children to help on to their immortal destiny, good above all to have given them such a mother as Sophie Barat. Philippine pressed her lips to the cold stones of the wall in gratitude and love. So, surely, must the Three Magi have kissed the rough stone wall of the dwelling that sheltered Him who was born King of the Jews.

The cold winter morning gave place in her mind to that scene in far-off Bethlehem. "I must pray for detachment like that of the Wise Men," she reflected. Detachment. It made them leave all in quest of the truth. There would have been perhaps mother, father, sisters, brothers, who would have pleaded not to be left. But God called. There would have been friends giving good sensible advice, acquaintances with the mocking word that cut deep, blank apathy from those to whom they spoke of the quest that urged them to leave all things. God detached them so that they should find Him. In the darkness of their night there was the star to beckon them on. But in the blaze of the Eastern day, there must have been long sandy wastes and treeless desert and days and weeks when they might have wondered whether their wisdom was indeed folly. She knew that heart-ache. It had helped to detach her in some measure from self-reliance. God's leading—could there be anything safer? His leading—not to the place one imagined, Herod's palace and sunlight amber on marble floors and a silk-lined cradle of gold. No. To the unforeseen. To an artisan's cottage in the grey of nightfall, with the star poised above. Unpredictable, but the Child was there, the reward of their detachment. They were within now, kneeling to give their gifts symbolic of their self-outpouring. Gold, the subject's tribute to his King. Frankincense, the creature's annihilation before his Creator. Myrrh, the man's acknowledgement of his identification with the Man of Sorrows. Lord, it is good for us to be here, here at our journey's end. But day was breaking, the bells jingled with the impatient shuffling of camels' feet, the Magi rose. Not the journey's end, but the start of a new quest. Detachment from the dearest place on earth to them now, to take their knowledge to those who still dwelt in darkness.

Philippine found herself looking at the stone wall of Ste Marie d'en Haut. The sky had turned from black to grey and the star had faded above the chapel. An eddy of wind caught up the snow on the hillside and twisted it round up into the air and away. An overladen branch of a pine tree let slide its white covering. She did not see or heed. In that moment her love for Ste Marie's, the child of her sorrows, slipped away from her. No longer did it hold her a prisoner. Beyond this white snowy mountain side, the world was peopled with men and women who knew nothing of the Child and His Mother. The Magi were taking the dusty sunbaked road to Persia—beyond lay India, and beyond again, China and the Islands of Japan. Prayer was not enough. There must be sacrifice too. There was but one thing to do. Her resolution was taken. A letter must be sent at once to Mother Barat. She would understand. She would see that when God had given her daughter so great a gift of detachment, action must not be delayed. She must go at once to the missions.

Posts were slow. It was nearly a month before her letter reached the Mother General at Amiens. Tears came into Mother Barat's eyes as she read, "I determined to offer myself to instruct the idolaters in China or any other distant lands."

Her heart overflowed with gratitude to God, and in the full tide of her happiness, she wrote back. Philippine read and re-read her words:

"Your letter was a very sweet consolation to me . . . I have been asking Our Lord for this ever since He put you in my care . . . I was convinced He expected this self-devotion, this complete sacrifice from you . . . Before ever I knew our little Society, the longing to carry the Name of Our Lord to the un-believing nations was at the bottom of my heart . . . St Francis Xavier became my patron . . . but one day a holy person I con-sulted told me, 'You are destined for France, you will not leave her shores . . . I know now I am Superior General she was right . . . but each day my longing grows and I pray that one of my companions may fulfil it and that the Holy Spirit Himself will lead her. . . I can't say yes to your request yet, but go on hoping. . . I used to want to pour out my heart's desires to a friend to whom Our Lord had given the same longing to make Him loved and known. I hope that more faithful than I am, you will set no bounds to His Mercies, and then it will be a con-solation to me if you can give Him the glory that He expects of us. . . It would be very consoling as you say, to preach Jesus Christ to hearts that are fresh and have not abused the graces of salvation, like so many here who are deliberately losing their souls. But we can't abandon these because they give more pain and less consolation. If only one was saved by our care, we ought to devote ourselves till death for her salvation."

Would it be China or America? Should she learn Chinese

or English, Spanish or Red Indian? How soon could she be a grain of incense burning in God's honour? When would she be sent as 'a lamb among wolves'?

Mother Barat wrote back pointing out the necessity of first being a lamb. Penance with prayer was good, but of little use if it wore her out before the seas could be opened again for French ships by the lifting of the English blockade. There was too much work in France as yet. She must have more common sense and patience. But she might pass the night of Holy Thursday in prayer before the Blessed Sacrament. The language of His Heart was the one most worthy of study for her mission.

On Good Friday, Philippine told her mother and friend of that vigil. "It was indeed a blessed night," she wrote while her eager joy was still absorbing her. "I spent it all in the New World, and I travelled there in good company. I began by kneeling in the Garden of Olives, in the Praetorium, and on Calvary, gathering up with all my love each drop of the Blood of Jesus, and taking hold of Him in the Blessed Sacrament. Clasping It to me closely, I carried my Treasure everywhere, with no fear of exhausting It. I saw St Francis Xavier standing before the throne of God, and I besought him to make this seed grow, and to open new countries for me to work in. St Francis Regis and many other saints eaten up with zeal for God's glory guided us on our way. No grief, however holy, could find room in my heart, for it seemed to me that the merits of Jesus were on the point of being applied anew to souls. The twelve hours of the night sped rapidly by, and although I spent them on my knees, I felt no tiredness, even though it had seemed to me the day before that I could not have stayed in that position even for an hour. I had so many sacrifices to offer up—a mother —and what a mother! sisters, relations, and then my own mountain home. I saw myself all alone, with little black savages around me, and I felt happier in the midst of my baby courtiers than the greatest ruler in the world. Dearest Mother, when will you say, 'Behold, I send you forth'? Oh, if it could only be be-

"It was indeed a blessed night. . . I carried my Treasure everywhere."

fore the end of the year! I almost hoped it would be. I am going
to try to be sad during the rest of Good Friday, but I don't feel
inclined to sorrow. My heart is turned to hope."

But Mother Barat saw further than Philippine. God would
not spoil His work by haste. The star had shone with no uncertain light, pointing the way. But the way for her valiant
daughter was to be no easy one. If she was to be a light to lighten
the Gentiles, she must shine with a steadfast beacon-ray. Conquest must be preceded by self-conquest. Time and again she
reminded her that they had much to do in their newly formed
society.

"Do be patient," she wrote, "and remember that God's
works progress slowly." But when she was in Bordeaux seeing
to the foundation of another house, she could not forbear to
send a message.

"While the novices who were going to Poitiers were crossing the Garonne, I stayed in the harbour watching them, or
rather, examining the ships which were alongside the quays in
considerable numbers. Soon my sisters of Bordeaux passed out
of my sight and out of mind, and I found myself on your mountain and then it seemed to me that we were both of us back here
again, ready to embark on one of these vessels to go at long last
where your desires call you. How I wished you could have
shared the sight of this fine harbour which all the same was only
interesting to me because of the thoughts it gave rise to."

So Philippine kept on with the little things of school life.
Amélie de Mauduit came and made her First Holy Communion
at Ste Marie's, Euphrosyne Jouve's bright mind and warm
heart demanded her loving watchfulness, the growing number
of pupils gave more and more opportunities for small acts of
devotedness. A ship left for China but she was not on board.
She looked for signs and tokens of God's Will, and was scolded
by Mother Barat for her lack of common sense, when she formulated hair-brained schemes for hastening God's hour. When
Mother Barat was not at Grenoble, things were worse. Sad and
full of doubts, one day she went out onto the terrace with her

Bible, and sat down beside the well. The book fell open at the sixth chapter of Deuteronomy, and she began to read: "When the Lord thy God shall have brought thee into the land . . . and shall have given thee great and goodly cities which thou didst not build, houses full of riches which thou didst not set up, cisterns which thou didst not dig, vineyards and oliveyards which thou didst not plant . . . take heed diligently lest thou forget the Lord who brought thee out of the land of bondage . . . that He might bring us in and give us the land concerning which He swore to our fathers."

She looked up, a sudden certainty filling her mind. Across the valley of the Isère lay the great mountain peaks set like a barrier, but now they seemed unsubstantial, fading away before her eyes. Beyond them stretched a vast horizon of lands where she would see houses of the Sacred Heart in the midst of great and goodly cities, full of the riches of the love of God, the waters of baptism ready to be poured out, the Wine of the Eucharist, the oil of Confirmation. When would this be? She did not know, but it would be so. An immense flood of consolation filled her. Then she went back into Ste Marie's to teach her class grammar.

While she corrected exercise books, Napoleon pushed the bounds of his empire ever further, and there were Bonapartes seated upon the thrones of Europe, and French armies in every country.

K

18: Passing Years

JEROME Bonaparte was a nuisance. No doubt the young American Miss Patterson was attractive, but he should not have married her, since he might have realized that his brother would have thrones to dispose of. The only course in 1808 was to get the Pope to annul the marriage and so leave him free to marry into a royal family. Napoleon felt himself powerful enough now to dictate to the sovereign pontiff. True, two years ago Pius VII had proved unexpectedly obstinate in refusing to close the papal ports to English ships or to expel Englishmen from the Papal States as the Emperor demanded, and Napoleon remembered, with an unforgiving pang, that he had been made to regularize his own marriage with Josephine de Beauharnais as a condition of his coronation. But now that he was master in Europe, he could exact the annulment of a marriage that stood in the way of his ambitions. After all, Miss Patterson was only a Protestant.

Pius VII refused. The marriage was in perfect order. There were absolutely no grounds for denying a perfectly valid sacrament. The Emperor tried intimidation. French troops were moved in force into the Papal States and into Rome. Virtually a prisoner, the Pope went on with his labours as head of a Church that was under no temporal power. He made three new bishops for the great tracts opening out in America along the Mississippi and Missouri rivers. In August an English frigate with cabins specially fitted out by Queen Caroline of Sicily approached Ostia, ready to rescue him and take him to a place of safety, but he would not leave his people and his city. In May 1809, flushed with his military successes, Napoleon cut short his pretence of being a second Charlemagne and issued a decree uniting all the Papal States with the French Empire. Rome was henceforward an Imperial City. Two hours before noon on 10 June the Papal flag was hauled down from the Castle of Sant'Angelo to the accompaniment of a discharge of artillery, and the tricolour floated against the blue Roman sky. But at nightfall the Pope had answered the outrage. On the walls of St Peter's, St John Lateran's and St Mary Major's was posted, for all to read, the Bull of Excommunication of those who fought against the Church of God.

"What does the Pope mean by threatening to excommunicate me?" Napoleon had asked two years before. "Does he think the world has gone back a thousand years? Does he suppose that the arms will fall from the hands of my soldiers?"

Now the threat had become a fact, he cared little. On 5 July, on his orders, a band of French soldiers broke into the Pope's apartments. The sight of the unarmed old man in his white habit gave them pause, but he allowed them to carry out their commands, and submitted to the indignities of the long journey by coach to his prison in Savona. On 20 July he was in the capital of Dauphiné, where he was welcomed "like a loved father returning after a long absence to his devoted family".

At four in the afternoon, the children of Ste Marie's crowded the windows that looked down across the Isère at the prefecture.

"There's the Holy Father's carriage driving in!" cried Mother Duchesne. "See, children, there, with the gendarmes all round it. Pray for him—you're looking down at one who is being persecuted for the truth as much as St Peter or the martyrs of the catacombs."

In the evening, they sent up from the prefecture to borrow a Missal and cruet for the Holy Father's Mass the next day. The

second day of his stay, Pius VII wished to see Reverend Mother
Deshayes. The third day, all the sixty children of the school,
dressed in white with black veils, went down the hill and into
the prefecture. They knelt in a semi-circle and kissed the
Fisherman's ring. Up in Ste Marie's Mother Duchesne burned
with desire to aid him. Each evening the whole household
gathered and watched him appear at the window and bless the
huge crowds gathered before his prison. Each evening he
raised his eyes and looked at the convent on the hill and his
lifted hand gave them a special benediction. But on the feast of
St Peter's Chains, they watched in vain for him. At four in the
morning he had been hurried into his coach and taken towards
Savona.

Life at Ste Marie's went on again in a round of school duties,
while the Holy Father withstood the Emperor who was planning the conquest of the world. Life had to go on as usual,
though no one could anticipate for how long. The religious
congregations were being suppressed. There were now no
longer any Fathers of the Faith to give them corporate help.
Two years later, even the Sisters of Charity came under the
ban. Who could foretell the future? In June 1812, it seemed very
dark, when Napoleon moved Pius VII to Fontainebleau. He
would be more in his power there.

At Christmas 1812 Josette de Saussure was home from
school.

"This is a much better report," said Henriette to her ten-
year-old daughter. "How have you managed it?"

Josette smiled with pleasure.

"Well, you see, Mother," she answered, "I've got Mother
Duchesne for my class mistress."

Frédéric looked up.

"Does she spank you?" he asked teasingly.

"Of course not!"

"I know what it is—she scares the life out of you and you
daren't do a thing—and I suppose you've saved all your wickedness up to plague your poor old father with in the holidays."

"Oh, Daddy, it isn't that at all," Josette said, with tremendous seriousness. "If you only knew Mother Duchesne—"

"I do," said her father with a laugh.

"I mean, if you had her for your class mistress—well, you'd just not want to be naughty. There isn't time. She tells us all sorts of exciting stories."

"What about?" asked Henriette.

"Oh, martyrs and things—Red Indians and Chinamen—and missions and preaching the gospel to the heathen and sailing the seas to go to foreign lands and—"

"And I suppose that if there was a boat at anchor in the Isère, you'd all be ready to go on board and sail away with Mother Duchesne," said Frédéric.

"Rather!" said his daughter. "Wouldn't it be lovely! And we'd be quite safe with her, because she knows how to look after us when we're ill and she's awfully kind to us and gives us all sorts of nice things to eat when we're not feeling well, and when we're feeling all right, she teaches us how to give up the nice things sometimes so's we can save the souls of heathens, and then she plays jolly good games with us—hide and seek and running round the building and dodging in the garden. She's ever so holy too."

"How do you know that?" asked Henriette.

"Well, Mother, we see her sometimes at night kneeling in the chapel bench, and she's praying so hard that we can creep right up close to her and she never notices, and one day I said, 'Let's put some bits of paper on her habit,' and we did, and then when we came down in the morning for Mass, she was still there and we went up and had a look and the paper was still there too, so she couldn't have moved all the night, could she, and we've done it several times and that shows you how she must pray, doesn't it?"

"My goodness, yes," laughed Frédéric. "My knees would get knobbly if you asked me to use them for five minutes."

"I can manage twenty minutes," Josette said. "And that's why I'm going to be good all the holidays. I've prayed, and

Mother Duchesne says if you pray hard enough you'll always get what you want. And I want to be good, and then perhaps I'll be able to go with Mother Duchesne in the boat. That's what Euphrosyne Jouve's going to do and all the big girls say she was just as naughty as me when she wanted to be—when she was as old as me, I mean. She's awfully nice now."

"I saw M. Duchesne this morning," Frédéric told his wife. "He's ageing, but he seems very happy in the midst of all his grandchildren. I thought he would have minded Mélanie's going to the Visitation at Romans, but he is quite content. He often goes to see Mother Duchesne at Ste Marie's. So do the Périers and the Jordans and all the other Duchesne relations—our Philippine is becoming quite an oracle for them."

"You might get some sense if you went, too," said his wife. "I don't know how you get on without the help of religion. Look at the political situation. We can't go on providing armies endlessly for the Emperor's conquests, and after this set-back in Russia, there'll be new recruitment."

"I met Colonel Dutour as well this morning," said Frédéric. "He was telling me of the retreat from Moscow—he was lucky to have been sent back on a special mission. There are others still dragging themselves across the frozen wastes. He says that on 15 September they were all secure in Moscow, as they thought, when the fires broke out. They had to watch the city turn to ashes, and then Napoleon decided they could not stay. The return began in weather that was mild for the time of the year, but when they were well away from the possibility of winter quarters, on 5 October, the cold suddenly struck them. He said it was unbelievably cold—an agony to endure, a nightmare to contemplate suffering for days on end. The men wrapped themselves in anything they could seize—they threw aside their plunder unless it was a garment of some kind or other. Then as the Grand Army staggered across the bleak snow-fields, their fingers grew numb, and the muskets fell from the hands of the soldiers."

Henriette shuddered.

"They are saying it wasn't the Russians that defeated the Emperor," her husband went on, "but the cold. When that is over, he will return as he always does, and bring with him an unconquerable army, and re-establish the tricolour."

"What a man!" Henriette sighed. "He has only to raise the eagles, and men come flocking to him. Why is it?"

"I think it's his strength and his steadfast purpose and his demanding the heroic thing from his followers," Frédéric reflected. "If a leader is like that, people will rally to him and be glad to follow if he goes ahead."

Twenty-year-old Lucille Mathevon knew that truth when she came from Lyons to Grenoble in 1813 and entered Ste Marie's as a postulant. She knew what persecution was, for her family had sheltered bishops and priests in the time of the Terror, and she did not want a quiet safe existence if there were honours to be gained in the fight. She warmed to Mother Duchesne when she found she longed to leave France to spread the truth.

"Perhaps we shall be able to go soon," she said. "Do you know what Cardinal Fesch has just said to us in Lyons? 'The Emperor is ruining himself. I foresee the time when he will be borne down and annihilated. All who touch the Holy Ark experience the same fate.' When the Church is free again, we'll be able to do Our Lord's work in distant lands."

M. Duchesne had chosen a fine warm day in the autumn of 1813 to call upon Philippine. He found a peaceful quiet at Ste Marie's, but his bones were stiff now and the hill took it out of him. They sat together by the parlour window and looked out on to the browning grass and the russet trees whose leaves were floating gently down to the ground. A mild blue sky melted into the dim purple outlines of the mountains in an indistinct haze. In the distance, there were the happy voices of children at play. His thoughts went back to other days when he would have been listening to catch the sound of her laughter in their midst. He remembered her golden hair and sparkling blue eyes as she used to run forward to meet him. That time seemed much nearer than the bleak days of the Terror, and the dark night when he had taken his daughter home again, and had seen the tears on her stricken face. He did not remind her of these times. They had not much to say to each other. There were things about which they would never agree. But always they would know that love lay between them.

"How swiftly the Isère is flowing," Philippine remarked. Her father smiled, still with his thoughts in the past.

"I remember watching it the day you were born and wondering what my next child would be like," he said. "A great deal of water has gone by since that August day forty-four years ago. And you live one side of the stream and I on the other. Well, well. I shall have to be going now. My legs aren't what they were. But it's a lovely mild day—quite an Indian summer."

Philippine took him to the door. He turned, clasped her hands within his, and said with a depth of tenderness that startled her, "Goodbye, Philippine."

Then the door closed on him. In a flash, Philippine knew that this was the last time he would climb the hill to Ste Marie's. Tears blinded her eyes.

Back in class, Josette de Saussure, with her father's love of words, had made a discovery.

"Mother Duchesne, Our Lord is a priest, isn't He?"

"Yes. Why do you ask?"

"Well, that's pontifex in Latin, isn't it, and pontifex means bridge-builder, doesn't it, and that means that Our Lord builds bridges, doesn't it? I wonder what rivers he builds bridges across?"

"Not the Isère," said her next-door neighbour.

"I don't see why not," said Josette with a laugh as she went on with her work.

That winter the grey storm clouds seemed a presage of the troubles that were awaiting France. On all sides, the Allies were rallying their forces. Men began to doubt the Emperor's power to recover lost positions. Others affirmed that he would gather his strength and fight and win a decisive victory. He could not, being the man he was, suffer final defeat. Philippine was praying for another victory. In January, Euphrosyne Jouve had come to tell her that M. Duchesne was dying.

"They don't think there can be any hope," she said. "Oh, if only he would give up that wretched philosophy of his—that's what makes him dislike religion, isn't it? And he's been such a good grandfather to us all, and he ought to get rewarded for that—Mother has just had two Masses said at Our Lady's shrine in Lyons. Oh, do pray for him."

"Do you think I don't?" said Philippine quietly, and Euphrosyne saw for a moment into the depths of her aunt's heart and was silent before the vision of year upon year of prayer.

When they sent up to say that they thought the end was near, Reverend Mother Deshayes called Philippine to her.

"As our rules of enclosure haven't yet been finally formulated," she said, "there is permission for you to go to your father. It's a soul that is at stake and it will be an act of obedience for you."

It was strange to drive down the hill once more. She crossed the bridge to the other side of the river, and soon she was at home. Mme de Mauduit and Mme Jouve left her alone with their father. He lay propped up on pillows, his fine strong face white and drawn but his eyes still steadily looking out on to the world and the little left of life. She saw he could follow all she said with his old alertness of mind.

"I know I am dying," he said, to relieve her. "The candle will soon be blown out."

"Father," she said earnestly, "you know that that is not true—your immortal soul is not a mere candle flame to be snuffed out. When death comes and your body lies here cold and powerless, your soul—you yourself—will be in the presence of God. All the false specious arguments of deists and atheists can be countered, but I won't try that now. I think you know now, as I do, that the Christian faith is as real as the air around us—in the face of the tremendous truths that have come down unshaken through century after century, your philosophy is thin and meagre and of little consequence."

"You are very sure, Philippine," her father murmured, and added with a trace of his old smile, "That's the Duchesne characteristic."

"It's more than that. I'm only a kind of mouthpiece for Our Lord—think how He has become man for love of you, and lived and laboured to teach you the truth that His Heart yearns for you with an unfathomable love—and if you doubt it for one moment, look at the crucifix and you'll see Love willing to be nailed there and to die for you."

"For me—" her father spoke softly. "Men are vile; vilest when they are ungrateful."

"But Our Lord's Sacred Heart knows that," said Philippine, "and still is ready to receive us sinners."

Pierre Duchesne's eyes were shut. He was seeing the chapel at Ste Marie's and the statue of Christ with bared breast and finger pointing to His Heart. His mind went back through the years and he saw himself a boy in white gala costume kneeling at the altar of St Andrew to receive the Bread of Life. That was before he read fashionable books that mocked at faith. He remembered how he had thought of himself that day like a young Bayard, placing his hands within the hands of his Liege Lord and swearing fealty, asking to be kept without fear and without reproach till the day of his death. Again he saw himself little more than a baby, standing by his mother's knee while she turned the pages of a book of pictures. They were grown-up ones and he did not understand many, but he remembered how he had put his hand on hers from time to time and said, "Stop." That was when the picture was one of Mary, Mother of God. Mother of God. Of course. How could he have lost that knowledge? Coming upon it again now was like a home-coming, a happiness that went to the very depths of his being. That was the happiness Philippine had. She would understand. He opened his eyes again. Philippine had been waiting a long time.

'You are very sure, Philippine. . . That's the Duchesne characteristic.'

"My dear," he said, "will you get a priest? Perhaps Fr Rivet? He lives on your side of the stream."

He did not die that day though he made his peace with God and had the Last Sacraments. In their strength he was able to have the joy of expiating in part for the years of forgetfulness by accepting his acute sufferings. When the end did come, Philippine was again with him, and as she closed his eyes her heart sang with triumphant gratitude. It was 27 March.

On the tenth a decree of liberation had set Pius VII free to return to Rome. The enemies of France were massing on all her frontiers. As the Republican deputy who had opposed Napoleon's ambitions in 1803 was borne to his grave, the noise of cannon shook the air. The garrison of Grenoble had sallied out to oppose the Austrian armies that were attempting to cross into France. These were the passing things of the world. Pierre Duchesne saw them now in the light of eternity.

To those who were left, things appeared to happen with unexpected swiftness. In April, the Emperor signed his abdication, "for there is no sacrifice," he wrote, "that he would not make in the interests of France." On 29 April he had sailed to take his empty title to the tiny realm of Elba. On 24 May Pius VII was in Rome again. By July he had decreed that the Society of Jesus should be re-established. The Fathers of the Faith hastened to offer themselves to the new General. Fr Varin and Fr Louis Barat exulted. After long waiting, God had gained the victory.

Europe took stock after the ravages of war. France looked for peaceful days under Louis XVIII. On 25 December four postulants entered Ste Marie's. One was Euphrosyne Jouve, another Octavie Berthold, a convert from Calvinism.

"In great and small things," thought Philippine, "we have much to thank God for."

But on 25 February a brig put out from Elba and two days later dropped anchor in the bay of Saint Juan. Then the rumour spread that the Emperor had returned and in his grey overcoat, with the Old Guard in their bearskins wearing the tricolour, was marching north. There was excitement in Grenoble.

"They are saying that the Emperor has prophesied that when he should be on French soil again, the Eagle would fly from spire to spire till it alighted on the tower of Notre Dame," said the convent handyman to Mother Duchesne. "I can well believe it. They're going mad about him in the town."

It was a hot noon on 7 March when Napoleon drew near to the city. The troops from Grenoble went out to intercept him and to end this new bid for empire. He drew near to their ranks, ordering his bodyguard to reverse arms. Alone in front of foes covering him with bayonet and musket, he flung open his cloak. "If there is a soldier among you who is willing to kill his Emperor, let him do it!" he cried.

The soldiers had but one answer. They left their officers; weeping with joy, they crowded round the man who could lead them by the greatness of his own example. The march into Grenoble was a triumph. With Dauphiné, France was won. Hearts grew anxious again for the peace of Europe. Only an old man in Rome in the Chair of St Peter remained calm. "This will be no more than a three months' storm," he said.

April passed and May. On 18 June Waterloo was fought. Napoleon kept his forty-sixth birthday while the English ship *Northumberland* bore him a prisoner towards St Helena. Philippine began to feel that her thoughts might again be free to plan to cross the seas herself.

In the early autumn, the superior of Ste Marie's, Reverend Mother Bigeu, was summoned by the Mother General to a general council of the Society. She took with her for companion Mother Duchesne. The community was thrilled. On 25 October they were at the door to see them off. "You'll see Reverend Mother Barat," they said, with holy envy.

"Never mind," said Philippine as she stepped over the threshold of Ste Marie's. "I'll be able to give you first-hand news of her when I come back."

When they reached the end of the alleyway, the two travellers turned and looked back. The nuns were still in the doorway and they waved goodbye. Then Reverend Mother Bigeu disappeared round the corner, and Philippine, lingering, saw them shut the door.

19: God's Hand

As they approached Paris, Mother Duchesne's thoughts crystallized into a certainty. With the superiors of all the foundations present and able to speak of the growing strength of the Society, it would be apparent that the hour for the missions had struck. She would be able herself to plead their cause, and to offer herself again. While the new Mother House was being prepared in the Rue des Postes, she would be free to make the necessary arrangements with all concerned in Paris, then return speedily to Grenoble to settle her affairs there and perhaps to gather up Euphrosyne who was now nearing the end of her noviceship and whose choice of the name Aloysia so well fitted her ardent soul. What would they not be able to do among the heathen together?

Emilie Giraud arrived from Niort.

"Well, Emilie," Philippine burst out as they greeted each other, "we shall really be going to the foreign missions—and you'll be coming, too."

At St Thomas's Convent where they were staying, she found the statue of Our Lady of Gras beloved of St Francis of Sales. Our Lady would give her her heart's desire.

Philippine spoke to Emilie Giraud, her old ally in praying for distant lands.

"I only want God's Will," said Emilie, wiser now after ten years of religious life and seeing apostolic work in her teaching of French children.

"What!" cried Philippine. "Is that all that's left of your old courage and zeal? What have you done with all your longing to convert the heathen?"

The Council met. They discussed the business of the houses in France. They appointed Philippine Secretary General. Henceforward she would be chained to a desk in Paris.

When Fr Varin called, Philippine reproached him.

"Can't you plead the cause of the Missions?"

"No," said Fr Varin.

"But you used to be so keen," said Philippine. "Why, it was you who told us at Ste Marie's that our care of children's souls would not be limited to Europe."

"I named no time," Fr Varin pointed out.

"But you gave me a promise that I should be the first to be sent out to the heathen—and when I asked your blessing, you gave it me, oh, so willingly!"

"I know I did," said Fr Varin, "but you must wait for God's hour."

"I think it has struck," suggested Philippine.

"No," the Jesuit answered. "Look at all that there is to do for your new congregation here in Europe—as secretary you should realize all that."

As secretary, Mother Duchesne was invaluable. Careful, accurate, self-effacing, a skilled letter-writer, she was an aid that Mother Barat could not do without. It was sweet to renew the every-day intimacy of work that had been their joy in that first year of noviceship at Ste Marie's, though paved streets and houses replaced greensward and distant mountain peaks. But dear as this was to Philippine, she could not rest while souls called to her from afar. She spoke to Mother Barat again.

"If I did tell you to go and convert the savages," said the Mother General, "what would you do without companions, money, or help—you can't expect Providence to grant you the privilege of walking on the waters. Wait. Go on praying. Perhaps later we can think about it. For the moment it's out of the question."

Only Fr Louis Barat, held in France to give missions to ignorant and indifferent Catholics while his heart roamed the wild forests of the Americas in search of savage souls, with rough hardships and perhaps martyrdom as his reward, only he understood and watched the heavens, as she, for the least sign. He, as she, was convinced of the need for prolonged prayer and persistent penance to wrest graces from God. It was as well that it was his sister, and not he, who had the ordering of Philippine's life.

"Take care of your health," said Mother Barat. "Strong as it is, it could not last a year if you went on leading the sort of life you want, and you must preserve it in order to work a long time for the glory of God."

When human means failed, there were still the heavenly hosts to mobilize.

Business took her through the streets of Paris. There was the little church on the hill of Montmartre where St Ignatius and his first companions had met and vowed themselves to the greater glory of God.

"Here St Francis Xavier offered the Holy Sacrifice," thought Philippine, as she knelt by the altar. "How could he with his great apostolic heart be deaf to my prayers?"

There were shrines of Our Lady at the Carmelites, at the church of the Foreign Missions, at St Sulpice. Heaven was bombarded with prayers. But as the months passed by, and nothing happened, she felt the need for earthly allies in her warfare.

She wrote to Aloysia, beginning her teaching work in Grenoble.

"Oh, do tell all our children to pray for the foreign missions."

She could count on her niece's own prayers being heard. She had refused God nothing, and her generosity had been linked with a rare perfection in all she did. How could God refuse her when she prayed?

Then God began to show His Hand. Mme Jouve wrote to

L

her sister in the May of 1816. She spoke of this and that, and because it was fitting to give ecclesiastical news to a religious, she mentioned that the preacher attracting the interest of the pious in Lyons at the moment was a certain Mgr Dubourg, lately come from Louisiana to try to get money and priests for his enormous diocese. He was a Creole, she said, and had a way with him. The good folk of that hard-headed commercial city had opened their hearts and their purses. Priests were rallying to him. Mother Duchesne smiled with joy. From Lyons to Paris—surely that was the way. But days stretched into months and the bishop did not come.

God showed His Hand again. Aloysia fell ill. An abscess formed on one of her feet. Medical science could do nothing to cure it. Another pierced her other foot. Soon there were open wounds in her pain-racked body. Mother Duchesne, in the midst of her sorrow, saw it as a challenge sent from heaven.

"I have obtained leave, since I have a deep sense of the needs of all countries where we are asked to work, to make a vow to St Francis Regis that if he obtains your complete recovery, I shall encourage your desire to be employed in the instruction of so many neglected souls in foreign lands," she wrote to Aloysia, wondering whether it would be to China or to America that she would be sent.

Aloysia smiled when she received the letter. Encouragement of desire! There was little need for that. But deep within her, she knew that God was taking that desire and refining it, removing from it all personal satisfaction and delight in the work itself, and uniting it to the pure desire that on the Cross cried, "I thirst!" She would labour and win souls in foreign lands by the purchase price of her sufferings in Grenoble.

In November, Bishop Dubourg went to Bordeaux. Fr Barat hastened to him. The two men discussed the needs of far-off Louisiana—needs of the old Catholic population, the French and the Spanish, needs of the new Catholic immigrants, Irish and American, needs of those rooted in the southern lands watered by the Father of Rivers, needs of the pioneers pushing north and west into the unknown lands about the headwaters, needs of the negro slaves working on the plantations, needs of the savage redskins retreating into their forest fastnesses. Fr Barat spoke of Mother Duchesne and her longings. The bishop listened eagerly. This was the Hand of God. In great haste Fr Barat wrote to Philippine.

"The matter is settled! There is nothing now to be done except to fix the time of your departure and the means of going. What is wanted are strong souls, and strong souls are not easily found, especially among women. You have so long pined for your savages that it is probable that God will make an exception in your favour and will not insist upon your being a strong soul."

But the matter was only settled between two unauthorized persons. Even Philippine realized that. Yet surely this was a pointer! More prayer would move her superiors. She began the novena to St Francis Xavier with hope and joy. On 3 December she went to Mass in the church of the Missions. At the epistle it seemed to her that God was speaking to the depths of her soul. "How shall they believe Him of whom they have not heard? How shall they hear without a preacher? And how shall they preach unless they be sent?" But God had not spoken so clearly to the souls of her superiors. They were not sharing her inspirations. Their duty was to safeguard the growth of the new society, and be no spendthrifts of subjects and resources. December passed and Christmas, the New Year of 1817 opened, the Magi came and went. In the Mother House of the Rue des Postes, business correspondence filled the working hours of the day. Mother Duchesne had perforce to offer trivial jobs for her great intentions. She was acting as portress on 14 January when the door bell rang. She rose and opened it. A big man stood there and she glimpsed the purple beneath his overcoat.

"I wish to see Reverend Mother Barat," he said. "I know her brother. Tell her I am the Bishop of Louisiana."

Like a flash of lightning, Philippine was up the stairs and had burst into Mother Barat's room.

"Now is the hour of Providence," she cried. "I do beseech you, Reverend Mother, don't miss the opportunity. You've only one word to say. I implore you to say it."

"My dear child," said Mother Barat as she rose to go down, "the bishop must lead the way by making the request. That will be a sign by which I can judge God's will."

After the interview, Philippine went to Mother Barat.

"Well?" she asked.

"The bishop said absolutely nothing at all," said the Mother General.

Philippine looked as if a knife had struck her.

"He's coming to say Mass here to-morrow," added Mother Barat, wounded, too, by her daughter's grief.

In the morning, the bishop sat at his breakfast table in the Rue des Postes and thought.

"There's prayer here," he said to himself. "That's the first essential for missionaries. They're poor and, I should say, used to hardships. That's another good sign. They're able to use their minds, too, if what I hear of their schools in France is true. They'd suit me. I could make good use of them."

Mother Barat came in and he began to tell her of his diocese in America.

"How glad I should be," he said, "if I could have your nuns there. Could you not let me have some of your daughters?"

Mother Barat thought, "This time it is the voice of God." Aloud, she said, "When this can be arranged, I shall have a person to give you who is ready to go."

"Your brother spoke of a Mother Duchesne," the bishop replied. "Could I see her?"

It was easy to send for her, and she was soon kneeling at his feet for a blessing, but for once Philippine could find no words to urge her cause. Why should she? God had managed things for her. When the bishop left the house, she was thinking with delight, "A few weeks more and then I shall be on my way."

Mgr Dubourg was pleased, too.

"A few months more," he told himself, "and I shall have these nuns to take back with me."

Mother Barat's heart was filled with joy.

"A few more years, and Philippine will be able to go where she has longed to work," she thought.

Wise and holy priests were astounded when they heard from Philippine of the proposal. Every detail of human prudence was against it. Perhaps, after many more years, it could be undertaken, but they were positive in their advising the Mother General to delay. She knew that they were right. With the passing weeks that brought no news of Monsignor of Louisiana, busy in Italy, in Holland, and in Belgium in search of recruits, Philippine found it hard to wait, and harder still to hold out against discouragement. Yet as she entered the choir on Ascension Day, the words "Go, teach all nations" sounded in her ears as though spoken directly to her, and all the wisdom of the world could not stop her heart burning within her.

"Shall I ask again to go?" she wondered. A great sadness filled her. "I have exhausted all human means," she thought, but the tabernacle was there before her. "It is for Thee, my God, to act now."

The very next day, the bishop came to the Rue des Postes. He asked to see the novices as well as the community, and he spoke simply to them of the great work that was in his hands.

"Yesterday," he told them, "as I said my office, there was one sentence that stood out, and would not leave my mind. 'Go, teach all nations.' That is the vocation, that is the calling of God."

Philippine's heart bounded again. Surely, surely, this was the doing of God.

But the bishop saw Mother Barat next in private. He laid before her the plans he had made for the religious she was giving him.

"But, my Lord," said Mother Barat, in grief and perplexity, "I cannot proceed at once with this. I gave no formal promise for this year—and my ecclesiastical advisers are strongly opposed."

Mgr Dubourg was not the man to be put off easily. He had set his heart on this. When Father Barat had been so positive, it was unthinkable that his young sister should hold out against the project. He pleaded, he urged, he insisted. Mother Barat could not be moved. Angry and disappointed, he rose.

"I am wasting my time here, Reverend Mother," he said, and made for the door.

Mother Barat rose too and unhappily followed him. There was a quick step behind them. They turned. The tall form of Philippine stood there, her eyes reading their faces and her heart turning cold at what she saw there. Impetuously she fell on her knees, clasping her hands in supplication.

"Reverend Mother, give your consent," she cried. "Your consent!"

Mother Barat paused. Her heart leaped up in prayer, and clearly God spoke to her.

"My dear Philippine," she said, "I do give it. Now I will try to find companions for you."

The bishop turned back.

"Let's go to the parlour again, Reverend Mother," he said, "and arrange the details."

He felt a happy man again. Happiness was too weak a word for Philippine.

In Grenoble, Aloysia lay now unable to move, with five open wounds to offer for the missions.

"Reverend Mother, give your consent."

20: Blue Peter

"IT'S strange," said Philippine at
the end of January, 1818, "that I don't mind waiting these last
months since the bishop returned to Louisiana. It's different
now that everything is settled. And of course there has been
plenty to do, what with nursing the children and nuns here,
and making things to take with us, and learning English. I wish
I was a better scholar. Octavie beats me when it comes to getting to grips with that illogical language. I shall have made
some progress I expect before we leave in June. Then once in
America I shall have to get down to the Indian dialects."

She pulled out a letter from Fr Barat and read with a smile,
"You are going to work among the Illinois. You had set your
heart on the Iroquois, but you are not quite holy enough to be
eaten by the Hurons and Algonquins. Thank God you will not
yet be devoured by the savages, but you must be eaten up by
the love of God and a fiery zeal for souls."

Mother Barat came in with a letter, too.

"Read this," she said, and watched the surprise flush her
daughter's face.

"Why, if the Vicar General is sailing in mid-February and
expects us to go with him, we've only a few days more!" she
cried. For once Providence was running ahead of her. But she
would not be left behind in the race. The projected work of
months could be telescoped into two weeks. Mother Barat

summoned her companions, hastily trunks were filled and packing cases nailed down. There would be no farewells with her family, no leavetaking of her dearly loved Aloysia. She had looked at Ste Marie's for the last time and had not known it.

"How can you keep so calmly happy in the midst of all this interviewing of tradesmen and merchants and people coming and going all wanting to see you?" asked the Mother Assistant, wondering at the radiant joy that was shining from Mother Duchesne's face as they packed a trunk together.

"Now that my relations have managed to get the passports through in time," answered Philippine, "I don't think any thing could grieve me. I'd almost be ready to make the greatest sacrifice and say, 'If only I go, I should be content to be superior.'"

The Mother Assistant looked at her. Was she the only one who did not realize what was in store for her? How could the work be entrusted to any other?

Mother Barat broke the news to her as the days drew to a close.

"My dear child," she said, knowing only too well herself the cross that she was laying on her daughter, "are we so far removed from the ages of sanctity? Can we not tread in the footsteps of the saints? When I think of what God has done for you, I cannot help hoping that since He has gifted you with an affectionate and grateful heart, you will love Him as great souls have done. You will be a mother to your companions. Octavie Berthold you know already since her noviceship days in Grenoble. How surprised M. Voltaire would be to see the daughter of his secretary leaving her country to teach savages to be true children of God! She will make her profession on 3 February. I wish all religious were as mature in holiness as she is at the age of thirty."

"Eugénie Audé I know, too, when she spent those first few months of her noviceship at Grenoble," said Philippine. "She's only twenty-six, but I think you would find her more apt than

I to be superior. She has a good head, and she's far more attractive to others than I am."

"I shall let her make her profession when she arrives from Quimper," said Mother Barat, ignoring the suggestion. "I think she, too, would astonish the gay circle that knew Mlle Audé at the court of Napoleon. You see, Philippine, how the sight of the Face of the Man of Sorrows can change our heart. Do you remember she told us how she saw His blood-stained features instead of her own in the mirror after a ball? You will have Sister Catherine Lamarre who has come from Amiens. Sister Marguerite Manteau you will pick up at Poitiers. You will have to have exceptional powers, since it may be many months before letters can reach us. You will have to admit or dismiss subjects, manage all financial problems, found houses, give employments, change your costumes for the time being if the religious habit is forbidden, dispense from the rule of enclosure if you have no chaplain. Take care of your health. You have one form of penance that takes the place of others—"

"Being superior," sighed Philippine.

"Yes. But you will be happy in doing God's Will. Your example strengthens me, but you've awakened all over again the desire I had for the missions. I can't help envying your lot. I don't suppose I shall ever share it. Anyhow, what use should I be? Well, pray for me."

"Pray for me," said Philippine. "My greatest happiness will be to form for you nuns worthy of the Society and of you. Otherwise, I'd rather die."

"If your going meant only that one Tabernacle more was opened, would that not be joy enough?" said Madeleine Sophie Barat.

On the morning of 8 February there were many who gathered at the Rue des Postes to bid Godspeed to the travellers. Fr Varin was there and Fr Roger.

"I once said it would be worth going to the ends of the world for Mother Duchesne," thought Fr Varin. "I know now that it is worth sending her to the ends of the world."

Octavie was in tears as Mother Barat enfolded her in her arms. Philippine, hiding her own grief, took her by the hand and with a smile drew her away through the door and into the street. The diligence was waiting for them. One last look at the friend who had been all in all to her, and she had turned to face the future.

"Let the man take the heavy bags," she said, and saw that her companions had places within. "We've a long journey before us."

The coach rumbled along through the Paris streets. The houses thinned, and they passed by fields where already preparations for the spring sowing had begun. The officer snoring in one corner roused sleepily. He cleared his throat and began to sing.

"Women and wine!" he warbled uncertainly, then tried a lower key. "Women and wine! Fill every glass, for wine inspires us and fires us with—" Memory failing, he set off again. "Women and wine—"

In the other corner a young man glanced up hastily.

"Heavens!" he thought. "This won't do for these ladies— nuns, I take it; in spite of their travelling dress, there's something about them. What a good thing I brought a breviary with me. You never know when things will prove useful."

He turned to the psalms and began chanting them aloud. The officer's repertoire of drinking songs was made more extensive by repetition. There was no pause, now that he was well launched.

"Black eyes and blue, Here's a bottle for you," he carolled.

"*Factus sum sicut uter in pruina*," the young ecclesiastic countered. "*Clamavi in toto corde meo, exaudi me, Domine.*"

"Fill up your bumpers, with a rifol rifoltoldiddle dee!" The military voice was strong if a little shaky on the notes. The psalms were not proving loud enough. But a hymn could be potent. Eugénie Audé began to laugh. The unharmonized duet successfully prevented any one from thinking too deeply of the parting. When they reached Orleans at nightfall, even Octavie's tears were dry.

They passed Orleans where Joan the Maid had shouldered her burden, Tours where St Martin had accepted his cross, then on the third day they were driving into Poitiers where Madeleine Sophie Barat had prayed for strength to bear the labours of a foundress. The narrow cobble-stoned streets led them up to the convent on the hill overlooking, with descending terraces, the calm waters of the Clain.

Reverend Mother Henriette Grosier was waiting with outstretched hands. She had shared the hardships and difficulties and joys of the beginnings of the Society at Amiens. Her heart was warm for these sisters of hers who were going to face the hardships and difficulties and joys of the beginnings in the New World. She led them along the stone corridors of the old abbey of Les Feuillants, not now to show them places hallowed by the monks Louis XIII had placed there, but to point out where Mother Barat had gathered the novices about her to explain the rule in those early days when she had said goodbye to Philippine on her mountain. Here it was she had stood and smiled to see Thérèse Maillucheau come from her ecstatic prayer to gather grass for the donkey at the voice of obedience. Here it was that they had sat under the stars in the warm night air of summer and sung hymns while a novice accompanied them on the harp. Here she had worked at her desk, and here she had prayed. The house at Poitiers was very dear to their Mother Foundress.

"And I often think it must be very dear to Our Lord," said Henriette Grosier. She asked Philippine to see the school and to speak to the eager little band of children. Her words were a revelation to them. This tall, austere-looking mother had a heart that was as big as a continent—even bigger, for she carried them in imagination across America to the Pacific Ocean and then onwards to China. She asked them to pray for the simple innocent souls she would teach, and in return she would beg their prayers for the children of France.

"I am leaving all things here as completely as if I were about to die," she told them. "I shall not return to France or see you, dear children, ever again in this life."

Like St Peter, leaving all things—what would be her reward? She spoke her thought.

"I want the great and ineffable consolation of learning that you are all fervent in the love of God."

The children burst out into protestations that they would be. Brown, auburn, golden heads bent forward, sparkling eyes tried to impress on their memory the sight of this first missioner they were seeing for the last time. In their midst, twelve-year-old Anna de Rousier suddenly saw clearly what it meant to love God alone. It was a bitter-sweet thought to Philippine that the next time she was surrounded by children, she would be looking into the dark eyes of black-haired Indians or little negresses. These in front of her were passing right out of her life. Never again would she see them.

Sister Manteau had come from Niort. They set off again the next day, through Angoulême south to Bordeaux.

"Look!" cried Sister Catherine Lamarre excitedly. "You can see masts over there!"

But Philippine was looking at the crowd that was gathered round the stopping place of the coach. In the midst, the Vicar General of Louisiana was making his way towards the nuns.

"I have a carriage to take you to your lodgings," he said, smiling to see them. Philippine's humility took alarm.

"Mother Audé, take the two sisters with you in the carriage," she arranged hastily, and made her way with Octavie Berthold to the public conveyance. But when she reached it, there was a crowd gathered and they pointed her out with warm applause. "There's the Superior of Louisiana! The tall one! That's her. The Superior of Louisiana."

She was thankful when the coach moved off, and more thankful still when they were safe in the convent of Notre Dame.

On 14 February, Fr Barat came to see them.

"There won't be any question of your starting yet," he told them. "The *Rebecca* is still at sea. She's expected in any day, but the gales are bad. She will have to recondition and revictual and take on board her new cargo, so you have some days before you."

"We'll make a retreat," said Mother Duchesne. Fr Barat smiled. He appreciated this miser of time for prayer, and the little community were doubly dear to him since they were going where he longed to go. He offered to hear their confessions. These were to be instruments worthy of God's work. As years before with his sister, he recognized God's Will to use them for great things.

"Your brother is famous for pushing on to perfection souls that hang back," Philippine wrote to Mother Barat, while Mother Audé added, "If the only grace I had obtained in this journey was that of seeing a saint, I should not regret having taken it."

"How kind Fr Barat is!" Sister Lamarre decided. "He's brought us sugar to take with us on the boat. He says we'll need it."

March opened and still the winds were unfavourable. But at last they knew that on the second the *Rebecca* had anchored in the Garonne. Sister Lamarre philosophically accepted each day as it came.

"I've got work to do now that our baggage has gone on board," she said. "It's like being soldiers in barracks—I've to do the washing of the few things we've got so that we'll keep next door to godliness."

The Vicar General, Abbé Martial, sent word to them on Friday, the thirteenth, that the captain expected them on board the next day at ten in the morning. At last the wind was blowing in the right direction. Their few bags were quickly packed. Fr Barat came to bid them Godspeed, his heart filled with holy envy as he raised his hand in blessing over the kneeling nuns. The sun was bright as they went down to the wharf. Sister

Manteau eyed with some disquiet the little boat that was waiting for them.

"It doesn't look very strong to do a twenty-mile journey down the Garonne," she suggested. "But at any rate, the water's calm."

They waved goodbye to the friends who had come to see them off. The boat put out and soon the towers and spires and roofs of Bordeaux disappeared in the distance.

"There's the *Rebecca*," said a sailor, pointing to a fair-sized sailing vessel anchored some way from the shore. Beyond it the widening waters seemed to lose sight of land, and whitecaps broke their grey surface. As their boat drew alongside, the waves slapped angrily against the wooden sides. They climbed on board. The clean salt tang about everything spoke of the open sea and stirred Philippine's feelings of content. Eugénie was delighted to explore the ship and find the low-beamed cabin where they would take their meals, with portholes that gave upon swirling water. Sister Manteau measured the length of deck which would be all their promenade for weeks to come. Octavie studied the rigging and furled sails and marvelled at the compass and instruments that would hold their lives in their keeping. At length it was time to go to bed. In their small cabin, they shared out the narrow berths.

"Is that my bed?" asked Sister Lamarre incredulously, as they pointed to the top one. "How do I manage to get into it?"

"Holy obedience," laughed Philippine. "Remember Maurus who did not sink when his superior told him to walk on the waters."

Sister Lamarre began to climb up. It was not easy and the others had to laugh at her attempts. She was in at last.

"Are you all right?" asked Philippine.

"There are hardly any bedclothes here," Sister Lamarre said, dubiously.

They handed a blanket up to her, but in the narrow confines of the bunk it was not easy to arrange it. Bump followed bump.

"Do be careful," said Philippine anxiously. "You will hurt yourself."

"The only thing to do," said Sister Lamarre ruefully, "is to lie still. I haven't room to move. But if I get cramp and can't sleep any more, God be praised for all."

But sleep came to them, despite the unfamiliar sounds of creaking timbers and rushing waters. A deep thankfulness filled Philippine's heart. The long waiting was over.

In the morning they dressed with some difficulty as the cabin rose and fell, and went up on deck. They were in sight of land still. The village on shore seemed familiar.

"Why, we're just where we were yesterday!" cried Catherine Lamarre.

The Vicar General was speaking to the captain and came across to them.

"Mothers," he said, "the wind has changed again. The ship can't put out to sea. Passengers are to disembark. We've found lodgings for you in Pouillac yonder. You will have to wait until the weather clears."

"Wait!" cried Philippine. "For how long?"

The captain shrugged his shoulders.

"How can I tell, madame?" he asked. "When it's a matter of winds and tides, we have to wait patiently on the good pleasure of the elements."

"On the good pleasure of God," murmured Sister Lamarre. "Well, I suppose Our Lord must have His little joke with us. But I wish He'd chosen a better day," she added as she watched the waves breaking over the boat that was to take them to shore. "Palm Sunday! We'll be getting martyrs' palms instead."

It was disappointing to find that they had to separate for their rooms in the village.

"This is just like being soldiers," laughed Sister Lamarre. "We get together for work and then the bugle blows for meals, and off we go to our own quarters."

"Thank God that with all the inconveniences we're in a

village where the people are living a Christian life," said
Mother Octavie Berthold.

"The townsfolk want us all to be their guests on Tuesday,"
said Philippine. "Fr Martial says we cannot refuse."

They escaped as soon as possible to the church. The village
girls besought them to make the Way of the Cross with them.
Philippine read the prayers while Octavie with her strong
sweet voice and Sister Lamarre led the singing. The Abbé had
promised them confessions, but instead he set them to work to
help the girls prepare the altar of repose for Holy Thursday.

"Nothing like waiting!" said Sister Lamarre. "Ah, well,
God be praised for all."

Praised for the gales that blew all Monday and Tuesday and
Wednesday, thought Philippine. Praised for the fine weather
that greeted them when Thursday dawned. The captain had
sent word the previous day that they should hold themselves in
readiness, and now they were off down the road to the quayside. The first golden light was breaking through the clouds in
the east as they clambered into the little boat that swayed and
rocked against the piles of the landing stage. Only when the
sailor shoved off with his boathook did a thought strike Sister
Manteau.

"That's the last bit of France we shall ever set foot on," she
whispered.

On board all was busy preparation for departure. As they
were helped up on to the deck, one of the passengers already
there murmured with disgust, "Nuns! I hope they've a black
cat on board as a makeweight!"

A small terrier came running across the deck, paused with
foot upraised while he sniffed inquiringly. Then he ran up to
them, tail wagging and ears back. Octavie stroked him.

"That's Corbin, Captain Tourneur's dog," said a passing
midshipman.

"We're going to be happy here," said Sister Lamarre. "God
be blessed for everything!"

As the *Rebecca*, with sails set, glided down the estuary,

M

Philippine was thinking of many things. How distant that
Holy Thursday seemed when she had spent the night in prayer,
gathering the Precious Blood and taking it to all nations in
every part of the world! How distant, yet how near! God was
fulfilling her desires, not again as she would have planned, but
in the depths of His All-seeing Wisdom. The coast pilot was on
board, seeing the *Rebecca* safely through the dangers of the
coastal waters. She had been given a pilot in her dangers, when
shoals and swift currents might have wrecked her. But now the
coasts of France were becoming dimmer as the open sea
stretched across all the horizon. The pilot's boat was lowered on
Holy Saturday. Now all the safety of the ship was the responsibility of the captain.

By Easter Sunday, France with Mother Barat, with Dauphiné and its mountains, with Ste Marie's on the heights where
Aloysia Jouve lay suffering, France had gone from sight. There
was nothing to be seen now but the angry waves of the grey
March sea. Reverend Mother Duchesne was there with her
community of four on their way to the New World.

21: Landfall

"GOD be blessed in all," groaned Sister Lamarre after seven days of tossing on a stormy sea. "Isn't America in sight yet? I'd no idea it was so far away."

Philippine thought, "One can offer oneself for martyrdom —but one doesn't know one's weakness until one is seasick. Heroism, lofty prayer?—it's been all that I could do to say, 'Thy Will be done.' Now that I'm over it, I know myself the better and that's all to the good. I wish I could get some proper food for Octavie. The soup doesn't look appetizing, with its thick layer of grease, and the meat it's made of is bad. It would be something if I could get her some fresh water—or even water, for that matter. When I ask for it, it isn't brought for five or six hours. Well, we have left all things for You, O my God. You are in the storm as well as in the calm. And Our Lady has sent us calmer weather on her Saturday."

The sun shone at last and the fresh air on the deck began to restore the passengers. The Abbé Martial thought he might manage to say Mass early before the other passengers were up and about. He would meet the nuns in a secluded spot each evening to give them a spiritual conference. He and the ecclesiastical student who was his companion were discreet; they had no intention of rousing controversial issues in a body of people who willy-nilly must see each other at close quarters for weeks on end. But left to themselves, the nuns were already making friends.

171

"I've come across three poor workmen who are going to make their fortune in the New World," said Sister Manteau. "They're hoping they may discover a gold mine if they're lucky. I'm sorry for them now. They're just sleeping on deck or in any hole they can find that gives them shelter. They're worse off than us—we have at least the settee in the saloon and the three berths in the cabin next door."

"Mother," said Eugénie Audé, "there's a lady who has asked if we would allow her to join in with us when we say our night prayers on deck. I don't think she's a Catholic but there aren't any other prayers said out loud."

Octavie said, "I nearly had to offer my handkerchief to the cook to-day to wipe away his tears of gratitude—he says he's so fed up with the grumbles of most passengers about their food—which he can't help, poor man—that it melted his heart to hear us say 'Thank you.'"

Sister Manteau remarked, "I could give him some lessons, all the same. He isn't very expert with his cabbage soup."

"Cheer up," said Sister Lamarre, "there won't be any greenstuff left soon to make it of. The cabin boy was telling me we're behind time already. He's a knowledgeable laddie. Only thirteen, and he's done this crossing twice. He told me this Monday we should have been well away and we've only reached the latitude of Lisbon. He got a map and showed me. And do you know, we're on the same line as St Louis! But he doesn't know his catechism. I told him what I thought of him when I bound up his finger for him. 'You've to look after your soul as well as your body,' I said. And I've put a patch on his shirt for him."

Corbin followed them everywhere, with wagging tail.

On 2 April they watched the Azores grow large and then fade behind them. The sailors were anxiously scanning the skies. By nightfall the wind was howling in the rigging and the waters below stirring and heaving themselves like wild animals waiting to be unleashed. The captain had paced his bridge in gloomy silence. When he took his place at the supper board

among the passengers, he answered their worried inquiries
shortly. Yes, they were in for another storm, and a bad one at
that. Two gentlemen from Bordeaux glanced at each other.

"They said before we left that we should be dogged with
ill luck with priests and nuns on board," one remarked half
aloud to the other.

"How dreadful!" cried a lady, overhearing. "Captain
Tourneur, did you never read the story of Jonas? Surely repeated bad luck must mean there's some one here that God is
pursuing? Can't you do something about it?"

Mother Duchesne had caught the drift of what was said.
She waited for the captain's answer. No muscle in his face betrayed his thoughts.

"Would you have us draw lots, Madame," he asked, "to see
which of us is drawing down on my ship the wrath of heaven?
Then, I suppose, it will mean pitching the guilty ones overboard."

The lady was silent. A few laughed at the thought. The
second gentleman from Bordeaux remarked, "That'd be better
than the whole lot of us being wrecked."

But the storm was upon them. As they ended their meal,
the star-studded sky seemed blotted out by the mountainous
seas that were running. The masts creaked and groaned as the
ship plunged through the waves, lifted high one moment, to be
plunged headlong the next down into gaping abysses that
seemed bottomless. The wind wrenched away a sail that tore
with a loud report, while the fragment left flapped furiously.
Above the roar of the sea, the sailors' shouts came like cries of
distress. Within their cabin, there was no possibility of rest for
the nuns.

"We'll pray," said Mother Duchesne, but the porthole
burst open and in a moment green swirling water was soaking
them through and through.

"At least the berths are washed well for once," said Sister
Manteau, as she mopped up, and put dry shawls in place of the
sodden blankets.

They returned to their prayers, but again the waves broke through and set their things adrift.

"God be blessed in all," said Sister Lamarre with chattering teeth as she wrung out her habit. "It gives you some idea of what the sufferings of Noe must have been."

In the morning the grey storm clouds hid the sun, and the grey light showed grey billows that swept over the deck or burst with a crash that shook all the timbers, then rolled pell-mell over the sides. There was nothing to do but stay below for day after day, while the storm raged, and the sailors became more depressingly silent.

"Our Lady is Star of the Sea," said Philippine. "We must pray more earnestly to her. We'll sing the *Ave Maris Stella* each night."

By the end of the second week in April the captain's face was smiling again.

"Ladies and gentlemen," he said with satisfaction, "the bad weather is coming to an end, and we'll get the breeze we need. You'll be able to sit out on deck and enjoy the voyage."

It was pleasant to find the ship gliding peacefully before a following wind on a calm sea. The sun shone warmingly. Spirits revived.

"We'll go on with our singing of the *Ave Maris Stella*," said Mother Duchesne, and each night in a remote part of the deck, they gave Our Lady their prayer and praise. The sailors listened. Sister Manteau's clear, true voice carried farther than she knew, and took them back in memory to other scenes. The captain got to know the hour of their hymn and listened with his crew.

"The men say that song's lucky," the cabin boy told Sister Lamarre as she darned his jersey. "The weather gets better as soon as you tune up."

Day succeeded day with the sun growing hotter in a blue sky. Only one thing was really hard to bear. The Vicar General was still nervous about their position.

"I shall not say Mass so often," he said. "And you will not

receive Holy Communion so frequently. There are Protestants on board who comment rudely. We shall have to reduce the number of confessions, too."

Mother Duchesne sighed inwardly.

"Make up for the loss by more prayer," she urged her daughters.

Sister Lamarre could not understand timidity when they were missioners out to spread knowledge of the truth, but she acquiesced obediently.

"God be blessed in all," she said, and made up by seeing that the cabin boy did not forget his catechism.

On 21 April the man in the look-out sighted a sail. The passengers speculated idly upon its identity, but the sailors took in the vessel's significance as she drew nearer over the horizon.

"That's a corsair, unless I'm very much mistaken," said Captain Tourneur to his First Officer. "What speed are we making?"

"Nine knots only," said the officer gloomily. "She'll overtake us in less than no time—look how she's built for speed."

"We'll try to get away," said Captain Tourneur and gave orders to increase the *Rebecca's* speed.

"Get down to your prayers, ladies," said a sailor hurrying by. "That's a corsair yonder."

"St Vincent de Paul, preserve us!" cried Sister Lamarre, with visions of Barbary pirates and sudden death. Each moment the ship seemed to draw nearer, though the *Rebecca* was answering to her crew's efforts sturdily.

"Eleven cannon, sir," remarked the officer beside the captain. He held a telescope to his eye. "They're uncovering the foremost. They've run up the signal for us to stop."

"We can't show them our heels and we can't put up a fight," said Captain Tourneur sadly, and gave the order to lower sails. The *Rebecca* slackened speed and was soon rolling gently on the blue waters. The passengers watched anxiously while a boat was lowered from the corsair's side. It drew near, a rope ladder was let down from the side of the *Rebecca*, there

was the sound of boathooks grappling, and then the officer
from their captor appeared. It was not a fierce moustachioed
face, sunburnt under a red bandana, with gleaming gold ear-
rings, that appeared, but a neat, pink and white young man, in
spotless uniform. In halting French he put his questions. He
must see the captain's papers. He and his men must make a
search of the ship. He must see the list of the passengers. Under
the compulsion of the corsair's watching cannon, Captain
Tourneur complied.

"I suppose you realize I am an American citizen," he said in
good English. The young man and his companions thawed.

"So are we all," he said. "We're doing a job for the States
at the moment—we'll have to search you—but there'll be no
plundering."

At the end of his investigation the young man handed back
the captain's papers with a bow.

"I am sorry we have troubled you, sir. We are satisfied you
haven't any Spaniards aboard. We took you at first for a
Spanish ship. We haven't any quarrel with a French vessel.
You are free to go on your way."

"That's the queerest corsair I could ever have imagined,"
said Mother Berthold. "He was acting as if he was part of the
American navy."

"I expect those men would call themselves privateers," said
the Abbé Martial. "It's a life of adventure they want—if there
isn't a war on, they'll prey on any ship. If there is a war, then
they'll fight under their country's flag. Well, you've seen some
real Americans. You'll admit that there is plenty of spirit in
them."

Hotter and hotter grew the weather. In a few days the smell
arising from the hold penetrated all over the ship.

"It's the wine barrels," the cook explained to the Sisters.
"Some of them have broken, and the wine's got all mixed up
with the water, and that's just as rotten as it can be. Look at
what it's doing to my copper saucepans, and the brass fittings.
It's making the woodwork round about go mouldy."

He ran his hand over some plates and basins.

"It's growing mould on these, too," he said. "I'll have very little water to cook with—we're getting short apart from its going bad. And the biscuits are turning rotten; even the weevils won't enjoy them."

"I wish there was a greater silence on board ship," Sister Manteau said to Mother Duchesne one night. They were seated in the saloon waiting for it to empty. Men and women came in and out, sat round eating and drinking, laughing and talking. They had no wish to sleep before midnight or rise early. The two nuns in their corner tried to snatch a little rest in the midst of the noisy conversation, waiting until the saloon was deserted to stretch themselves on the settee.

"This is what any who leave France to help us will have to put up with," Mother Duchesne thought, as she lay sleepless in the early hours. "They will have to be strong in body as well as in soul if they are to survive. These airless cabins, the berths so hard and small, the noise of the rigging and cordage being manipulated all through the night, the ceaseless talking that sounds louder at night than in the day—and now this foul smell that there's no escaping—it isn't only courage but health that is wanted to get from France to America. How long a week can be!"

The winds of May were capricious. On Sunday, the third, they had crossed the Tropic of Cancer. But the wind veering, the ship recrossed the tropic. Five times she was driven to and fro. On Sunday, 10 May, Pentecost came with the sound of a mighty wind. A deluge of rain struck the ship and the gales grew more and more violent. With alarm the passengers watched the sails being lowered, and the helm abandoned. The ship was left to drift before the storm. She shuddered when the waves struck her, but she stood the strain.

"We can't do this indefinitely," said Catherine Lamarre. "Either the storm will end, or we'll be wrecked. Well, God be praised for all, whichever it is that happens."

Whit Monday dawned clear and fresh.

"It makes you think of Elias and the still small voice after the whirlwind," said Mother Audé. "God seems to be very near us now. There's a feeling of hopeful promise in the air."

Later in the day, a cry from the sailors brought them all running to the side of the ship. A faint line showed on the distant horizon.

"That's Caicos in the Antilles," Captain Tourneur explained. "An English island—we shan't be touching it."

"But isn't it good to see land after seven weeks of nothing but sea?" said Mother Audé. It put a new spirit into everything. They could look forward now, without the temptation to look back regretfully to the Old World. The New was already beginning to show them its charms. A school of porpoises came speeding through the waters and gambolled around the ship. Flying fish flashed gleaming through the waves. The blue depths changed colour with the scintillations of myriads of polyps. Even running on to a sandbank on Whit Tuesday did not seem so alarming. It was only a matter of patience until they should be lifted off again by the full flood. At day-break they watched the sun rise from ruddy waters in unimagined splendour, and at nightfall when the heavens grew dark and great stars shone in their thousands, the black waters brightened with the sparkling of phosphorescence. On Whit Saturday, they were anchored off Havana. Mother Duchesne wrote to Mother Barat with a heart full of gratitude.

"A year ago to-day at this very hour, nine a.m., we were receiving the last visit of the Bishop of Louisiana and you then gave your consent to a foundation in the New World. Happy as I was, I did not dream then that the anniversary would find us so near the goal of our journey, for what are a few hundred miles as compared to the thousands which we have already traversed?"

"There's a gentleman from Havana wants to see you, Mother," said Sister Manteau.

He was on deck with outstretched hands.

"I'm like the man of Macedonia and you are St Paul," he

said. "I want to say, Come over and help us—help us here in Cuba. We need schools for rich and poor alike. Will you come?"

Philippine's great heart was torn. Why could she not multiply herself? Why were there not more nuns to do all that needed to be done? Could not the Lord of the Harvest send more and more labourers? Perhaps in the years to come, they might return. Now the Indians beckoned them on to the forests of the Mississippi.

"We cannot come to you now," she said sadly.

The man pressed some money into her hands, a generous gift of forty piastres.

"You'll need it, Mother," he said. "You've God on your side like St Teresa, but even she didn't despise the necessity of having three ducats as well. We shall wait for you to come some time."

Mother Duchesne's prayers laid foundations as they skirted the flower-bright shores of Cuba. There were souls crying out everywhere to her. But God's finger pointed her to the city of St Louis.

A week later, on Monday, 25 May, the cabin boy called them to the side of the ship.

"Do you see there?" he said, pointing excitedly. "There's a sort of dark line across the sea? Well, that's where the Mississippi waters run into it. You'll see when we get a bit nearer. It's all muddy beyond."

They watched the blue sea mingle with the river. The *Rebecca* was now sailing on the Father of Waters. The legendary stream swirled by beneath them, a reality at last.

"That's the pilot's boat coming out to us there," said the cabin boy. "It's pretty dangerous along here with sandbanks and mudflats. Do you see that mudbank that we're sailing by? The men who live on it don't think anything of giving false signals and wrecking ships. We'll be sounding our way all along now till we reach New Orleans."

"Do we get there to-day?" asked Mother Audé.

The boy laughed.

"Not us. It'll take the best part of four days if we're lucky."

But they were four days packed with interest. As the river narrowed to a mile and a half in width, they could see dense shrubberies lining the bronze waters, and hear the wild scream of bitterns or the startling cry of cranes. At night fireflies twinkled, and here and there they caught the light in a cabin window. Once they ran on to a sandbank and once the sailors caught a small alligator.

"I don't mind one that size," said Sister Lamarre, watching its yellow mottled black skin. "But I don't like the look of the big ones we passed. This is only like a lizard."

"It's good to eat," said the cook, and he carried it off to his galley.

Now there were great plantations, and big white-walled houses glimpsed through the groves of pines and oaks. They watched duck taxi along the water and take flight, and curious huge-billed pelicans splash into the river. In the trees there were cardinals and black-beaks and blue bishops, and they caught the note of the mocking bird. There were fields of grass that moved in the breeze like the ocean they were leaving behind them, and best of all, there were negroes. They saw them at work on the bank, bending over the plants in the fields, driving the cattle in leisurely style, or lazing at the water's edge.

"We're nearly there," cried Sister Lamarre on the morning of the twenty-eighth.

"And all the mosquitoes of America have come out to meet us," said Mother Berthold, with her face red and swollen. "I couldn't get a wink of sleep for their buzzing, and look at poor Eugénie's cheeks. She's almost eaten alive."

"It's extraordinary!" the Abbé Martial greeted them. "Ten weeks to the day since we left France, and we shall be at New Orleans to-morrow, the Feast of the Sacred Heart! Providential! I shall say Mass for you on board. It's extraordinary!"

In the early morning quiet, with the tawny waters gliding smoothly by the portholes, the nuns knelt in the cabin at the

Vicar General's Mass. For the first time under an American sky, with their hearts too full for words, they renewed their vows and received their Lord. All the day long, as the ship crept slowly up the river and the country became more smiling, and wide fields of cotton and maize betokened men and women and souls precious in the sight of God, Mother Duchesne repeated to herself, "I have consecrated myself to Poverty, but how rich I am in You. I have pledged myself to Chastity, but You are my soul's delight. I have vowed myself to Obedience, but to serve You is to reign. I dedicate myself to the education of youth, but You are the Shepherd of their souls."

When evening fell, they were still twenty miles from the city, but a message came at seven to say there were two carriages awaiting to drive them to their destination. By eight they had packed their portable belongings and were up on deck. The other passengers gathered round, eager to shake their hands and to wish them Godspeed. The cabin boy, with tears in his eyes, hung on to Sister Lamarre's hand. The cook let his dinner cook itself and joined the sailors taking a last look at them. Corbin wagged his tail and bounded round them as Captain Tourneur said goodbye to Mother Duchesne.

"I've never been better pleased with any passengers I've had," he said. "We're all sorry to lose you."

Her thoughts flashed back over the trials of the voyage. With an inward smile, she answered, "I shall always remember the *Rebecca*."

The sailors had lowered the pulleys of the landing chair, and one by one they were swung out in it and down into the rowing boat. With rhythmic dip of the oars, they drew near to land. Above, the dark blue sky shone with luminous stars whose reflections in the black water broke into fragments as the oarsmen drove the boat onwards. Mother Duchesne had her eyes on the bank where fireflies lit the low bushes. Eugénie Audé, glancing at her, was awed. Tears were in her eyes, but the joy that radiated from her face was something that seemed a foretaste of heaven.

"Surely," Mother Audé thought, "that is the joy that only the Heart of Jesus could inspire—and inspire only in a soul filled with His grace and bent on glorifying His Sacred Heart."

They were by the shore now and the sailors held out helping hands to tide them over the verge. It was marshy ground that they stepped on to—but it was the soil of America. God had brought them at last to the Promised Land. Mother Duchesne fell on her knees, overwhelmed with gratitude, and kissed the very ground.

"No one is looking," she whispered to the other four. "You kiss it too."

There was the sweet scent of magnolias and orange blossom in the air, as they walked to the road. From a copse a mocking bird burst suddenly into rapturous song. The horses stamped, impatient to be off. The Abbé Martial gave the word and they were away. Sights, sounds and scents, all were those of another world, but before them, as behind them, Christ was in His tabernacles, the same for ever.

It was past two when they drove into the city. They caught fleeting views of wharfs and quaysides and bales piled high, and open market places; then they turned into the old quarters of New Orleans, and passed silent shuttered houses with iron, traceried balconies, and doors opening on to courtyards where fountains splashed. A cathedral spire reared up.

In the hush of the small hours the narrow streets might have been those of some southern French or Spanish town. But a lonely passer-by was singing a hauntingly sad melody and the carriage lamps lit up his features and showed white eyeballs set in a black face. This was no midnight dream. These were American streets they were traversing.

They pulled up at length by a door in a high-walled garden. Beyond they saw the plastered grey buildings with steep tiled roof, where for close on a hundred years the Ursulines had lived. They waited in the chaplain's house until the six o'clock Angelus rang out. Then they knocked at the convent door.

Apologies for the unwonted time of arrival were swept away in the warm-hearted welcome of the nuns within.

"If this is the charity of the New World," said Sister Manteau, fortified by Mass and a proper wash and well-cooked fresh food and a clean room that did not shift and sway beneath her feet, "I shall wonder what we've come here for. It's we who will have to learn, and not to teach."

"But this is New Orleans," said Mother Berthold. "This is not our final destination. We have come for the savages."

"God be blessed in all," said Sister Lamarre.

22: Upstream

MOTHER Duchesne fastened the last strap on her baggage. They would soon be going down to the quayside to board the river steamer *Franklin*. It was 12 July and they had reached New Orleans on 29 May, and in all that time there had been no word from Bishop Dubourg. Six weeks of waiting, six weeks full of so much that was new and interesting and puzzling and perturbing, six weeks when she had felt how far they were from France and the Mother who could have counselled them and cheered them, six weeks in which she had realized that she had now to be such a mother to her companions and bear the full weight of their anxieties alone.

She knew now that the ideas they had formed of their mission so many thousands of miles away had not been true. What was romantic about them had faded before the reality. Only the reality of souls to be saved remained. She had begun to see this the very day of their arrival at the convent of the kind Ursulines. The portress had called them to the parlour door to see their first Indians. The two men stood there in their tunics belted in at the waist, a woollen cloak knotted at the neck and their long black, greasy hair falling over their shoulders, willing to be gazed at, so be it that some coins were forthcoming as the price. There was a pitiful look of sadness on their faces, and Octavie had whispered in surprise, "Why, there's nothing savage about them." Since then she had seen others, dregs of men, ragged and ignoble, with drunken slatternly women and dirty children. Perhaps in the virgin forests to the north-west they kept their manhood.

They were not the only men who made the lovely rose-tinted Crescent City like a blossom that hid a canker. When she had gone down to the port to get their cases of goods, she had seen the greedy unscrupulous traders from all the countries of the Old World and the sharp-faced, money-minded Americans from the north all bent on seizing the chance of exploiting the wealth of Louisiana. She had heard from the Ursulines of pleasure-loving girls who left school to marry, caring only for position. In the negro quarters there were crime and vice—men who were bought and sold like cattle acted like the brute beasts.

But in the first three days there had been also the small coloured child who had run to her, clasped her about the knees, and turned her round black face upwards with sparkling eyes of love. And there had been many other coloured children to whom they had taught catechism in the classes held at the convent, and she had seen how naturally they had given their love to their Father in Heaven. There must be schools for them where God's image cut in ebony should sit beside His likenesses in ivory and bronze. Souls were all equal in His sight. If the equality of men meant anything at all, it meant this. There would be coloured nuns, too, in the habit of the Sacred Heart, bearing on the cross they wore the reminder that they were one heart and one soul in the Heart of Jesus.

She could hear in imagination Mother Barat's prudent acceptance of her ideas. "Wait, Philippine, the time is not yet ripe. You will ruin all if you try to hasten God's hour. Wait. It will come."

Here and now there was work in plenty to do, and she recognized all the wisdom of the advice they gave her in New Orleans to make her foundation in this growing town where educated French-speaking women could do so much in all grades of society. In St Louis it would be English that was needed

N

straightway. She had realized in these weeks that, for her, that language would always be baffling. Octavie was a natural linguist, Eugénie darted her contribution into any conversation in English, in a determined effort to acquire it, but she herself could not understand, in the softer, more drawling pronunciation of these Southerners, even those few words that she had managed to learn in Paris.

The man from Cuba had again come to her. There would be no financial worries about a foundation there. The Abbé Martial had hinted that there was no house ready for them in the episcopal city and that the price of land was fantastically high. Yet St Louis was where Mother Barat had meant them to go, following the desires of their bishop. Holy Obedience would keep them safe, even if it did not smooth away difficulties. God had already given evidence of His protection. The ship that had left Bordeaux after the *Rebecca* had been lost at sea. The *Rebecca* herself on her return journey had been boarded and pillaged by the pirates that lived on the mudbanks of the Delta. She knew, too, that He meant her to go forward to the Indians.

That truth had emerged from the illness that had struck her down soon after her arrival. The doctor who diagnosed scurvy had looked serious and death had come near. She had not been afraid—rather, it had seemed very sweet to think that she had been allowed to enter the Promised Land and could now hand over her charge to Mother Audé, who would manage it so much better than she. She had smiled to remember how Mother Barat had once teased her with the story of the Jesuit who, after years of waiting, had landed in America, baptized one soul and then died. She had been piqued then: now it seemed to her that it would be the best thing if she could be removed from a work which her lack of virtue would only hinder. But against all expectations, she had made a good recovery. God meant her to go on.

There was a knock at her door. Mother Berthold and Sister Manteau were there.

"The carriage is ready for us," said Mother Berthold. She looked quizzically at her superior. "You look quite different in that poke bonnet and black dress with the thin white stripe. Thank God, we don't follow the fashions!"

"If we must wear secular dress and thinner material," said Mother Duchesne, with a laugh, "I think we've done very well. I'm not so sure about the dark purple the Sisters are wearing— but the cut doesn't encourage vanity."

"When we get to St Louis," said Sister Manteau, "it'll be like putting on celestial robes to get into our habits again."

"And entering heaven," Mother Berthold added, "to have a house of our own at last with an enclosure wall round it."

Mother Duchesne was silent. Would it indeed be like that? After all, they were embarking on this journey of thousands of miles upstream without any directive from Bishop Dubourg. She had made the decision after waiting in vain. It might be that when they reached St Louis, he would not want them. But she would not spoil the hopes of her community by her secret anxieties. They picked up the baggage and went to the convent door. The Ursulines gathered round, pressing on them last-minute gifts of comforts and money, and promising help and prayers in the future. Then the green door in the white adobe wall closed behind them and they were driving through the old narrow streets to the harbour.

The *Franklin* was berthed in the midst of a medley of craft. There were sailing vessels waiting to move down stream. Some were bound for the south seas and Mother Duchesne's mind leaped ahead and planned foundations in Japan and China. Aloysia should go there, wresting her cure, by sheer audacity, from God. She would be young enough to learn Chinese. There might be martyrdom too in Korea. "There seem no limits to my ambition," she thought with a rueful smile, "but I think it would end at that point. After martyrdom, I should have nothing more to desire."

But their way lay upstream with the flatboats and barges and rafts, on the newest of civilized inventions. What two

years previously had been a journey of four months could now
be done in forty days. It would be more a pleasure trip than a
preparation for laying down their lives. They went all over the
steamer, with bluff Captain Reed showing off her points.
There was her hold loaded to full capacity, the first deck that
held the strange machinery—oily engine and sooty furnace and
steamy boiler and inescapable dirt—and the deck passengers
herded in the small space behind. There were the quarters for
the cabin passengers on the second deck, a dining room, a
lounge and bar where already tough-looking men were drinking and filling the air with tobacco smoke, and the ladies' parlour right at the rear. The captain left them there, while he
mounted to the pilot house on the hurricane deck.

"It looks as if we are going to be comfortable," remarked
Mother Duchesne. An overdressed woman sat down beside her
and nudged her.

"Don't you believe it, my dear," she said. "Do you know
why we're put here? Well, it's to keep us out of the way when
the boiler explodes. They don't talk about that in the advertise-
ments, but I've done this trip before, and I know. You'll see
several of these steamers with the water washing through them,
as we go along. The last time the boat caught fire. You watch
now we're starting off—see all the sparks that come out? Well,
it doesn't take much to set this old matchbox alight. Still, that
gives a bit of variety. Nothing to look at for more than a
month—do you play cards?"

Mother Duchesne shook her head. "But surely the river is
interesting," she suggested.

"It gives me the creeps," said the woman, turning the rings
on her hands. "It all looks so smooth and then before you know
it, the boat's run into a great snag and there's a hole in her side
and gallons of dirty water to drink. Or in this sort of hot
weather, the sandbanks catch you—"

"But the captain must have charts—" began Mother
Duchesne.

"I don't know about that, my dear," said the woman.

"They wouldn't be much use anyhow, for the channels are always changing. It'll not be so bad if the men are a lively lot— we can have some singing and play cards. Of course, they may be a quarrelsome lot, and then you've to look out for bullets and knives. Have you seen the sleeping bunks? It's a good job they've put mosquito nets on them—but you can't go about on deck in a mosquito net."

She moved off.

"It doesn't look as if this is going to be a picnic after all," said Mother Duchesne to herself.

It seemed even less inviting as the day wore on.

"These Americans don't know how to cook," thought Sister Manteau, struggling with salted pork.

"It's queer that they serve no water at table," said Sister Lamarre, watching the amount of whiskey that some of the men were drinking.

"This will teach us not to be faddy," Mother Duchesne remarked as she watched a bucket of Mississippi water being shipped for drinking. "It's muddier than the Seine."

There were twelve people already in the ladies' cabin when they went to bed. Mattresses were spread on the floor in all direction.

"Heavens! I nearly trod on a baby," whispered Sister Lamarre as they picked their way to a corner.

"Me go to bed in there! I ask you!" grumbled an old lady standing at the door.

"You can't stay out on deck at your age, Ma," said a woman.

"Can't I! I've not lived eighty years for nothing," she retorted, and shut the door.

It was very close within.

"God be blessed for everything," thought Sister Lamarre. "I suppose I'll get used to this in time."

Rhythmic snoring might even prove a lullaby. At least there was no talking. Sleep came at last to all of them, and peaceful hours of forgetfulness.

"Can't you make room for me?"

They all awoke with a start. At the open door the old lady was standing, with the early morning sky still dark behind her.

"It's that cold—" she said, and edged her way in. A baby roused and whimpered. Sympathetically the other children joined in. There was a general stir.

"Well, Ma, perhaps you'll stay in another time," said the overdressed woman.

"Perhaps I will, and perhaps I won't," answered the old lady, settling herself on Mother Duchesne's mattress.

"I suppose it'll be morning soon," thought Sister Lamarre with cramp in her arms and legs, and the crying of babies in her ears.

Meanwhile in his episcopal palace of stone, cemented with mud, poorer than the poorest of French farmhouses, Bishop Dubourg waited anxiously for an answer to his letter to the nuns. Not knowing that it had miscarried, he wondered whether the austere future he had held out to them had proved too hard for their courage. He remembered his wording:

"You say you have come to seek the cross. Well, you have taken the right road to find it. . . Foundations always mean sufferings. Remember St Teresa. . . A thousand unforeseen difficulties may arise . . . one must plough before one raises a crop . . . you and I must spend our lives in this thankless task."

The wind blew through his unglazed windows, covering the place in dust. He realized that what he had said sounded grim, but surely he had not been mistaken in the woman he had met in Paris. Unforeseen difficulties: of these he himself had plenty. There was the hostility of some of his diocesans, the annoyance he had roused over building a cathedral more worthy of the Lord than the log barn he had come to. There were debts that seemed crushing. There was shortage of priests, and invalid priests, five of whom he was even now sheltering in his palace. If he could face such things, he could surely ask Mother Duchesne to accept similar trials. This little band of chosen workers would be his nuns, ready to do what work he wanted in the circumstances that he offered them. Mother Barat might expect in distant France that her daughters would open their school in St Louis. Here he knew that that was impossible. The house he had rented twenty miles away at St Charles was what he wanted for them. They were American nuns now, and must adapt themselves to American conditions. They would have him for father instead of Mother Barat for a mother. But suppose they did not come? Suppose he had not read them aright?

The *Franklin* was pursuing her leisurely course up the Mississippi. Each day unfolded some new beauty of landscape or lighting. The levées that gave a clear edge to the river, the spacious white houses, the piers gay with pleasure boats, the fields of cotton and corn, gave place to forests that came down to the water's edge, with great trees fantastically draped with Spanish moss. Here and there they passed the openings to bayous, covered with huge water lilies with cups of gold or pink or white. The shallow swamps showed grey twisted stumps of trees that seemed to take them back to the beginning of time, and when the sun rose through the dawn mists, in a hush broken by no bird songs, it was as if light broke for the first of days. The long undulations of Louisiana fell away behind them, the tropical vegetation disappeared, and the steamer wound through hardwood forests with maples and catalpas and flaming blossoms of the trumpet vine.

Cramped in the narrow decks of the *Franklin*, the nuns could yet let their spirits roam over vast horizons. There was so much to invite them to prayer—and so little on board to make it possible. In the saloon, there was noisy talking and raucous laughter, card-playing and gambling that sometimes broke out into angry disputes. The shouts of the pilot were heard through the chuffing of steam and the rattle of the engines. Ever and anon the loud clanging of a bell warned that danger was ahead, and fussily, with churning paddle-wheels, the *Franklin* would alter course to avoid sand bars or the sunken skeletons of giant trees brought down by the spring floods. At night the peace of the river was broken by the alarmed shouts from passing boats that narrowly escaped collision, and the lookout men, peering through the night with the light of torch baskets of smoky pitch, yelled warnings to the accompaniment of the clanging bell.

Week followed week, and there was no opportunity of going ashore to hear Mass, yet everything around them cried out for the supreme sacrifice which alone could give God His due. How else could they adore Him for the marvels of His creation, from the flight of tiny birds rising from the limitless forests, to the evening star that hung in the red sunset sky? How else could they thank Him for all His care of them, from their setting out from France until this moment? How else could they atone for the ignorant or wanton evil of the drunken men and disorderly women who crowded into the saloon? How else could they ask for the graces to win the souls of the Indians for the Great Spirit?

On 11 August they reached the place where the Ohio flowed into the Mississippi. A priest came on board and they found he was an old friend of Fr Barat, a great-nephew of Bossuet, who spent his life among the Illinois.

"He needs as much eloquence to move the hearts of these Indians," said Mother Berthold, "as his great-uncle preaching to Louis XIV's courtiers."

"More, perhaps," said Sister Manteau. She had been struck with the pitiful looks of those she had seen encamped in forest clearings or bartering their hunting spoils for bottles of whiskey at the landing stages.

"It's the grace of God, anyhow," said Sister Lamarre.

It was the grace of God that they saw when the boat put in to Kaskaskias on 17 August. The seed planted by the Jesuits before their suppression had grown, and the Catholic Indians still lived a Christian life gathered round their seventy-year-old pastor, who wanted nothing more for his comfort than two rickety chairs, a worn-out table, a mattress, a pitcher, and a mug. He took the nuns to the tabernacle in his church, and they knew then the source of his content. When the *Franklin* moved off again, the chief of the Illinois was there on the bank with his daughters and his braves. Curveting on their horses, with feathered headdress and beaded garments, they seemed at last the noble savages that had been the dream of the French nuns.

The *Franklin's* voyage was drawing to a close. Her fuel ran out, and the passengers were put ashore to help the crew gather wood. Her larders were empty, but the wild turkeys did not escape the guns of the men. Pounded maize took the place of flour for bread. Most of the passengers were ill through the heat but at least there had not been an explosion, and no epidemic had resulted from the poor sanitary arrangements of the steamer.

At Ste Geneviève, Fr Henri Pratte came out to see the boat. He found Mother Duchesne and recognized her worth. The young man had his whole heart in his growing parish, and he begged her to come there for her first foundation. They spoke together of possibilities. She told him of her Superior General's desire that she should have her house in St Louis. After that, it might be a good thing to start in Ste Geneviève and Kaskaskias, where French was still spoken, and Indians, already half civilized but unspoilt, could also be taught. Then there would be the foundation at New Orleans whose milder climate would make life possible for other more delicate nuns, and where a school for coloured children could be the model of others set in the midst of slave-owning peoples.

"See how I stretch forward when my foot is not yet firmly placed," she thought, "but desires are unruly when one sees so much need."

Fr Pratte gave her a letter of introduction to his brother in St Louis. "He has five little girls," he said with a laugh. "That'll make a beginning of your school! You will find him the very soul of kindness. Don't hesitate to accept his help."

The lime-stone cliffs grew steeper as the river bore them nearer to the city. On the evening of 21 August the *Franklin* anchored a mile from the Market Street landing, with its last

log burnt. The white houses could be seen boldly gathered together, with wood-covered hills rising in the distance. A sudden thought struck Philippine as she drew out her Bible and
found a chapter in Deuteronomy, as once before when she sat
dejected by the well at Ste Marie's.

"Hear, O Israel," she singled out, "thou shalt go over the
Jordan this day. Say not in thy heart: For my justice hath the
Lord brought me to possess this land. Therefore love the Lord
thy God and observe His precepts and ceremonies, His judgements and the commandments which I command you this
day."

The hills she was looking at were not the steep heights that
she had watched when first those words had promised her the
fulfilment of her hopes. She had learnt much since then, though
then she had already understood more deeply than in her early
days. There would no doubt be much more that she had to
learn, but it was always God who taught, God who had brought
her all the length of the way to cross over this Jordan.

Sister Lamarre came up to her.

"Mother Berthold is in the boat—the captain asks if you're
ready."

Kind, bluff Captain Reed—he was acting as God's deputy
to bring them to the land of their vocation. The rowing boat
took them up stream, they landed, and climbed the unmade
road, rutted and dusty, to the episocpal palace. There was no one
to announce them at the doorless entrance, but within was the
bishop. Not now in the speckless parlour of the Rue des Postes,
but in a tumble-down, unfurnished barn, these two great missioners met again, and each inwardly saluted the greatness of
the other, while they made arrangements for the morrow.

As he conducted them back to the *Franklin* for their last
night on board, Captain Reed realized the nuns were happy.
Well, they deserved to be; quiet, agreeable persons who had
given him no trouble throughout the journey. It must be
pleasant, he thought with a sigh, to be settling down in peace,
without the worries of a steamer on their minds.

23: Houses Filled with Riches

MR Bernard Pratte shut his account book, replaced it in the tidy ranks of its fellows, and went across to the door of the stores. As he closed and locked it, Thérèse, lying in wait, sprang out and seized his arm. They walked towards his house in silence for a minute or two, though he knew his little daughter wanted to ask him something. At last she spoke.

"Daddy, can't I go with Emilie and Céleste to Mother Duchesne's school?"

"There isn't going to be a school," he answered shortly.

"But—but—that's why she's come to St Louis," said Thérèse. "There's got to be a school."

"Go and tell the bishop that," said her father.

"Doesn't he want it?"

"Not here," her father answered, and explained, "You see, the nuns are very poor and they can't afford to buy land and build a house."

"I wish I was dreadfully rich," said Thérèse. "Then I'd build one for them."

"I don't think that would work the trick. The bishop has found a house for them at St Charles and he wants them there. I offered to let them rent a house I had bought here but he disapproved and they wouldn't disobey the bishop," said Mr Pratte, not sure whether to be angry or in admiration before such respect for authority.

Thérèse looked crestfallen. "Why at St Charles? It's miles away."

"He thinks that village will soon become a great town," said her father.

"Will it?"

He shook his head, with all the commercial intuition of a successful business man.

"No. Not for many years. The settlers are going beyond it. They'll just be frittering away their money—two thousand francs to rent Widow Duquette's six-room cabin—it's preposterous and I'll not be a party to it."

Emilie and Céleste joined them, Céleste almost in tears.

"What's the matter?" asked Mr Pratte.

"Mother says the nuns want you to hire a wagon for them to go to St Charles and you won't," Emilie explained. "And if they can't have a school here or there, they'll go away and then we'd never be able to be taught by them, and they're so nice."

"I can't have you twenty miles away." Their father was gruff. "Three or four months in the year, when the Missouri floods, I'd not even be able to visit you."

Twelve-year-old Thérèse, who had not for nothing been used to getting her own way, read the signs of his hesitation.

"Pélagie will go there, you see," she said. "I heard Aunt Chouteau say that she'd be ready to send her anywhere with Mother Audé—she said she was so distinguished. And if Pélagie gets distinguished, I want to be distinguished, too. Mother Audé's taught me how to make a curtsey like the French girls."

She demonstrated. Mr Pratte admired. They really were worth educating, these charming daughters of his.

"And Mother Berthold's taught us some hymns," said Emilie strategically. "She says we're just like the French girls."

"Only considerably more spoiled," said their father grimly, and refused to say more. But when that evening Mother Duchesne again spoke with him, he agreed to her proposal.

"It's against my better judgement," he said. "Your Mother

General thousands of miles away knows better than the bishop on the spot."

"The bishop is kind, but firm," said Mother Duchesne.

"Obstinate," commented Mr Pratte, wishing that the nuns' funds from France had not been deposited with Mgr Dubourg. "I've seen enough of you in these three weeks I have been honoured to receive you, to know that your judgement is sounder, too."

"God will look after us," said Mother Duchesne. When on 7 September they left St Louis, however, the thought filled her mind: "This is the tomb of our enterprise."

The bishop came on horseback to accompany them. Fr Richard, who was to be their parish priest, drove them. The five Pratte girls wept bitterly in spite of the fact that Emilie and Céleste were soon to join them, and the coloured children who gathered in the street to see the departure cried in sympathy. The fields were still bright with late summer flowers each side of the dusty road that led them nearer to the blue hills sloping down to the Missouri. They overtook a covered wagon beside which slaves walked prodding on cows that stopped to pull at grass by the wayside.

"That's what folk call a prairie schooner," Fr Richard explained. "This is a road that leads on to the far west, and unexplored tracts where enterprising settlers can be masters of the land. St Charles is the last village of the United States." He pointed ahead with his whip. "There lie your Indians, Mother Duchesne."

"Not in St Charles," the bishop riding alongside hastened to add. "There will be half-castes there, Mother, but the Pawnees and the Illinois are beyond."

They were dropping down, now, to the Missouri. Other covered wagons were waiting their turn to be ferried over the rich brown waters, sunburnt men and women and children looking with curiosity at the first five nuns who had ever reached that spot. There were Indians there, too, who came forward and silently offered their help and carried boxes and baggage up the hill on the far side, refusing payment. The road climbed steeply to the little church of St Charles Borromeo, then straightened out a little. On the next rise stood a log cabin. As they drew near, they saw its stone foundations and slanting roof of pegged shingles, the five-foot-wide verandah, and the two windows, one on each side of the door.

"Here is your convent," said the bishop. "The first house of the Sacred Heart in America."

With the houses of Amiens, Poitiers, and Ste Marie d'en Haut in their mind's eye, the sight of this house was disconcerting. They were to be Americans, without any doubt. This wooden step in front of them really was the threshold of a new life. The place was so unexpectedly small that Mother Berthold and Mother Audé burst out laughing, and went quickly forward. The bishop turned to Mother Duchesne, his face alight with pleasure.

"See these young people—they might have shone in any circles and yet here they are so gay! It's splendid, splendid! You and I are only old sinners."

Mother Duchesne looked at the garden. There were apple trees, pears, and yellow plums, and beds that had once been well cared for. Now there was a tangle of weeds over everything and the shrubbery was overgrown. Behind, the hill levelled out again, and showed hazel bushes and wild hops, while right up the road, here and there the roofs of the village could be seen. Looking back, she saw the muddy Missouri spreading out into a wide bay. The sunlight made it sparkle, and there was a tiny island set like a green jewel in its midst. Beyond on all sides lay the hilly open country. That was the world they were leaving, to be an island set in the midst. Like a jewel? Thank God, the young ones would be, though she, an old sinner, could only help them in the smallest ways.

Mme Duquette was at the open door, smiling and friendly.

"I shall have just one room for myself," she said. "The other four small ones and the large one in the middle are for you. I shall keep myself to myself, but if you need any help—"

They received it from her at once. The cases that had journeyed with them all the way from France had to be unpacked,
and Mme Duquette's furniture arranged to best advantage.

"We'll make the big room the chapel," said Mother
Duchesne.

The altar was set up. Over the tabernacle they put the
statue of Our Lady. In France, it had not seemed large; here
her head nearly touched the ceiling.

"Let's put this darling picture of the Nativity on the right,"
said Sister Lamarre. "And the Magi on the left. There's one of
the coloured men arriving at Bethlehem—this other King has
a bit of the look of an Indian, too, don't you think?"

"And the third king is us," said Sister Manteau, busy with
nails and hammer. "There are two pictures of the Sacred Heart,
and both from Rome, in this box—what's that one you're unpacking, Mother?"

"It's St Francis Regis," said Mother Duchesne. "It's not a
great work of art, but I came across it years ago in an attic at
Ste Marie's among some lumber. That was when the Magi's
star was not shining clear. I promised I would honour the saint
if he helped to light me on my way. Well, here we are, and the
bishop is going to dedicate this house to him."

On Our Lady's Birthday, the first Mass was said by Mgr
Dubourg. The new-born convent was under the protection of
the new-born Queen of Heaven, too.

When Sister Manteau brought him his breakfast, the bishop
asked, "Well, Sister, have you everything you want?"

"It's kind of Your Lordship to inquire," she answered.
"We shall do very well in a bit. There's no water in the well,
but Mme Duquette says a man will bring us buckets from the
Missouri at five cents a bucket. We shall have to be careful with
it, or it will be expensive."

"But you could get it yourself, Sister."

"It's out of enclosure, my Lord," she said.

"You'll have to drop French ideas of enclosures in America," said the bishop. "I shall have to change all that."

Sister Manteau flushed.

"My Lord," she said apologetically, "it's part of our rule—
you couldn't really change that—I mean, we should be different then."

After his meal, he found Sister Lamarre sweeping the
verandah.

"It's a queer country, my Lord," she said, when he approached her. "Not a wall anywhere as far as I can see. Our enclosure wall is a bit like the equator they learn about at school—
an imaginary line drawn round. I can't see that that's going to
keep people out of our property."

"America isn't France," said the bishop. "You'll have to
modify your ideas now. I shall want you to move more freely,
and to do active works of charity. You won't need an enclosure
wall."

Sister Lamarre was aghast.

"Excuse me, my Lord," she said. "I don't like to have to say
it, but I don't think Mother Barat would like that. Enclosure
means we've to put prayer first in our lives. Whether there's a
wall of stone or brick or wood fencing or a bit of broken wire
or even an imaginary line, I want to be inside it. That's where
Our Lord put me, and that's where I've the grace to stay."

Bishop Dubourg looked for the choir nuns. Mother Berthold was finishing her office.

"As soon as we can, we shall say it aloud in choir, my Lord,"
she told him.

"I've been considering," he said. "With so few of you and
so much to do, once the school has started, you had better stop
saying office. There must be some modifications in your rule."

"My Lord," said Mother Berthold with firm courtesy,
"that is our tribute of love and gratitude to Our Lady. It helps
to keep us heavenly minded. If we lose our prayer, we shall be
nothing more than school teachers."

He sought out Mother Audé. She had shown herself alive
to the needs of a new situation.

"Mother," he suggested, "you are in a young country.

Traditional ways will need to be weighed well. What you did in France may not succeed here. You must be ready to change with changing circumstances. I shall count on you to support my suggestions."

Mother Audé looked at him in alarm.

"My Lord," she said, "I am ready to do the utmost that I can to help you, but I could not support anything that meant changing our rule. You've seen Mother Barat. You must know she is one of God's saints. And He entrusted the drawing up of our rule to her. I could not tamper with it."

Impatiently he made his way to Mother Duchesne.

"Mother, as superior, you must see that I shall have to re-constitute your rule. Louisiana is not Dauphiné."

"Louisiana or Dauphiné, we are still nuns of the Sacred Heart, my Lord," said Mother Duchesne.

He grew red with anger, then burst out laughing.

"Well, you're five heads in one bonnet!" he cried. He would have to wait before he made alterations. He could not but admire their constancy.

There was plenty to exercise it in the next months. On 14 September they opened the free school. Twenty-one children presented themselves, noisy, unkempt, undisciplined.

"They've more dresses than chemises," said Sister Lamarre, looking at the grubby flounces, "and with all their finery, they haven't handkerchiefs."

"They don't know anything about God, or heaven, or hell," said Mother Duchesne. "When I teach them about Our Lord, they stare in amazement and I keep on having to say, 'Mind, it's all true.'"

On 3 October Mr Pratte drove up with Céleste and Emilie, and their cousin Pélagie Chouteau. The boarding school had opened. He brought a packet of letters from France. It was an unlooked-for joy to find one contained a blessing from Pius VII. Mother Duchesne remembered how, as a prisoner in Grenoble, he had raised his hand in blessing towards Ste Marie's. Now, a free man in Rome, he stretched it beyond the seas to

these "good, courageous nuns". What did the present hope-
lessness of their situation matter when they were doing God's
Will? Some time there would come for them, as for the Holy
Father, the change of God's right hand. So they went forward.

Some six day children came to join the boarding school.
Slowly its numbers rose to nine. Mother Berthold's command
of English grew. Mother Audé delighted them with her charm.
Mother Duchesne filled in all the gaps in their instruction in
French, but even the poor children were beginning to need
English.

"We've no savages yet," the nuns complained to the bishop.

"Indeed you have," he said, looking at the untrained girls
in their schools. "Your work with these will be lasting and
farther reaching. These rich children will be in positions of
influence."

Already the nuns had made a difference in the neighbourhood. The free-school children could sing Benediction. They
sang Fr Barat's hymn to the Sacred Heart. They sang for the
First Communion on All Saints' Day. They came on Christmas Eve and sang carols with the boarding school until the
Midnight Mass. They learnt to sing a Missa Cantata, and their
singing opened the way for grace in the hearts of the men and
women who heard them. They saw Mother Duchesne painting, and begged for little pictures of the Sacred Heart to take
home.

"The Church at Portage des Sioux has pictures of Venus
and Bacchus in it," said Mother Duchesne. "I used to be able
to paint—even my daubs would be better than those."

The nuns made paper flowers to put on neglected altars.
They were tokens of reviving, careful love. The children grew
happy, and learnt well, and their parents recalled truths they
had forgotten. The love of God was something real.

But there was a price to pay.

"Did you learn to do that at the Court of Napoleon?" the
bishop asked one day as he came upon Mother Audé milking
the convent cow. "They're glorious women," he thought.

"With all their culture, there they are digging and weeding and carting manure and cleaning the stable. Why, white folk here would count that as slaves' labour."

The winter came. Ill-fitting doors and windows let in the cold.

"Well I never," said Sister Lamarre. "The clothes I put by the fire to dry are frozen stiff."

"We ought to put more logs on the fire," said Sister Manteau, "but they're all too big. I wish we could get someone to chop wood for us—or get a saw to do it ourselves. Even the Missouri is frozen to-day, so there's no water in the house."

"And no bread either," said Sister Lamarre. She told their plight to Mother Duchesne.

"I thought the day might come when we should have no bread," she answered with a smile, "but so close to the Missouri I couldn't have dreamed we'd be without water."

"And I've only got bear's grease for cooking," Sister Lamarre added. "If you're writing to France, couldn't you ask for some oil—only tell them to see it doesn't leak. It'll spoil the books they're sending and the seeds for the garden. But we'll need it if we're to get through the winter without butter and eggs, and only salt fish for Lent."

Once or twice they had been startled to see the sky grow red with a prairie fire, but the wind had kept the flames away from St Charles. On Holy Thursday, it was within their own chapel that they had to fight a fire. A draught caught the white muslin hangings with which they had tried to make the sanctuary a worthy resting place for the Blessed Sacrament, and they had blown into the candle flame and blazed to the ceiling. The dried beams smouldered and sparks flew. But the water butt and gutters held the rain that had fallen the day before. With buckets passed from hand to hand, the nuns drenched the room. Hot and smoky, they stopped at length when the danger was over. With keen sorrow, Mother Duchesne approached the altar. The chalice was overturned, the pall and corporal were charred, but as she lifted the blackened fragments, she saw the

Sacred Host lying white and untouched. Reverently she replaced it in the tabernacle while her heart sang for joy. God had
remained, though all else was gone. What did it matter, either,
that coverings, floor, partition wall were fit only for the wood
pile? The statue of Our Lady, the relics, the picture of the
Sacred Heart were unscathed. These were their gages for the
future. There would be songs for the month of Mary, and
songs for the month of the Sacred Heart.

All the time there was the wearing anxiety of lack of means.
The bishop might speak of educating the rich, but very few of
the few boarding-school pupils could pay well. Some indeed
paid, but the banknotes they tendered were so much waste
paper, as in the financial depression that spread through Louisiana, bank after bank failed. The day-school children could not
afford to pay for books or sewing materials. The nuns could
not spare money for a gardener to till the garden that might
have helped their larder. The American postulant, on whom
they built hopes of further help with the English that was a
necessity, came and went. In spite of Mr Pratte's warm adver-
tising, the boarding school did not grow. The unsatisfactorily
small house would not at the best take more than sixteen. The
rent ate into their resources. But they had won a place in the
heart of the people of St Charles and plans were afoot to build
them something better.

Then the bishop, who had tentatively talked of alternative
plans, made his ideas plain. He had bought a large farm at
Florissant across the Missouri. There, under the direction of a
Trappist father, a convent should be built for them. He would
use the money he had in keeping from Mother Barat only on
this. At Florissant, their school would do well. Their lease of
the Duquette house was over. His arrangement was the only
possible one.

Mother Duchesne's heart fell. It was hard to desert St
Charles just when good was coming from their labours. The
little hamlet of St Ferdinand had scarcely more than forty
rough houses. The expense of building would be crippling for

years to come. The house would not even be ready for them when they went in September, and they would have to live in makeshift conditions that would scarcely attract pupils. And worse than all this was her certainty that St Ferdinand in Florissant Valley was another place right off the map. But in one of Mother Barat's letters, she had written: "The Bishop has spoken and he is the mouthpiece of the Will of God for you."

So on the first Friday of September 1819, two little boats took on board all the nuns' baggage and Mother Audé, Sister Lamarre and three children, and bore them ten miles along the stream. Mother Berthold and the two other children skirted the river in a carriage. Sister Manteau and Mother Duchesne gathered together cows, calves, and chickens. But the cows revolted. Nothing would induce them to set out in the heat. The nuns must wait. Early the next morning the last of their furniture was packed into three small carts. Angry at being tied, the cows again refused to move, but a few cabbages made them change their mind. Perched on a pile of luggage, Mother Duchesne kept her eyes on a case of relics and on the poultry beside her. At last the river was reached, and their belongings safely ferried across. Tenderly Sister Manteau gathered her cackling, scratching poultry round her and gave them water. Then they set off for the farm house that was to shelter them until their own convent was ready. They came upon it, a lonely place in the flowery valley. Mother Duchesne pulled at the leather thong that lifted the latch, the rough hewn door swung open, and they entered their new house. It was only a bare room, some eighteen feet square, with a loft above.

24: Frontier Work

"THIS is a very spacious city to which we've come," said Sister Lamarre. "There must be at least fifteen or twenty houses in it. Ah, well, the Lord be praised. Settling in doesn't take much time. No beds to have to make, as it's only a matter of rolling up a mattress and cover—dormitory, classrooms, parlour, refectory—they can all be swept at one go, and you don't ever need a dustpan, for all the dust goes through the cracks of the floor. It's easy to do without a portress too, when you can see people coming through the open door."

People came for interest, for curiosity, for business, or for spiritual help. They entered freely into the one room and sat for an indefinite time on the few chairs. They found the experience a pleasing one, while Mother Duchesne was forced to take her class into the garden, and Sister Lamarre wondered where she could find a corner to say her prayers in. It was fortunate that the golden autumn weather let the nuns wander in the property. From their hilltop they could see the cornfields harvested. The maples of the woods turned to flaming red. There were late strawberries to be found, and fruit to be gathered from the bishop's apple trees. There were bluejays busy among the elder bushes' berries, and the tapping of woodpeckers came from the forest's verge. Rabbits sat out in the slanting rays of the evening sun as the nuns and children took their recreation among the trees, and the wild roe deer would

206

come to them at their call and nuzzle their soft heads against
them, watching trustfully with big mild eyes. On their first
Sundays, they went down to the church of St Ferdinand, seeing
with astonishment the many horses tethered outside, for all the
world like a horse fair. Sister Manteau found it hard to recognize the poor housewives of weekdays in the grand ladies with
ribbon and flower-bedecked hats, coloured shoes and em-
broidered dresses, strolling along beneath their parasols.

"I am thinking there's a besetting sin of worldliness in this
land," she said, with the French peasant's thrifty view of life.
The neat purple uniform with its black velvet pipings worn by
the boarding-school children could scarcely vie in splendour
with the silks and satins of some of the free-school scholars.

The bishop's treasurer, Fr de la Croix, had left the farm
house and taken up his abode in an empty corn crib. Old cam-
paigner as he was, used to all the worst that Missouri weather
could do, nevertheless the winds that blew through his bird-
cage of a dwelling laid him low. Mother Duchesne's motherly
heart went out to him. Sister Manteau was bidden to cook the
daintiest food she could, while she herself doctored him and
tried to make him more comfortable. She sent word to the bishop. At once the order came that a log house should be built
for him. Ready hands among the farm labourers who had learnt
his worth put up a one-roomed shanty and added a second room
to serve as chapel. As soon as he could, the priest said Mass, and
the Blessed Sacrament remained in the chapel. From the attic
above dried beans and maize fell through, and with the growing cold, the draughts through the chinks of the walls were icy.
But the nuns were happy.

"He who has Jesus, has all," said Mother Duchesne, and as
she watched the growing school of nine pupils gather ever
closer in affection to Mother Audé, she saw her own part in
their life at Florissant grow more clear.

"What good shall I be, as I cannot speak English?" she
thought. "Octavie should replace me as superior when we
have more Americans than French-speaking creoles." She was

struggling to put a calf into the stable when the thought struck her, "How better suited I am to an employment like this!"

Then she remembered what she had said to Mother Barat in those distant days nearly two years ago.

"Even if I do nothing but cook for priests, I shall be glad."

As she had looked after Fr de la Croix, so she would mother the poor priests whom the bishop sent out to Florissant to recuperate from their missionary labours. They had no one to cook for them. It was fitting that they who gave souls the Bread of Life should receive sustenance for their own worn-out bodies. It would be easier to help once they were in their proper convent.

At Christmas time, the Trappist father sent them word that it was ready. On 23 December Mother Audé saw to the departure of the six oldest girls.

"Keep still, while I pin this blanket round you," she said, down on her knees with a pile of wraps beside her.

"Brrr! It's cold!" said Emilie Pratte. "I put my nose outside and nearly got frost-bite."

"That's why I'm putting shawls round everyone's head," said Mother Audé.

"How comic we look!" laughed Pélagie Chouteau. "It's a good job you've left our feet a bit free—otherwise if we fell into a snow drift we'd never get out."

"Sister Lamarre looks as bad as the rest of us!" said Céleste.

"A whole family of Indians, that's what we are!" chuckled Sister Lamarre. "Emilie's father, Pélagie's mother, and the rest of you the children."

"And what about you, Sister?" they chorused.

"Me? I'm grandma, of course."

"What sights you all are!"'said Mother Duchesne, highly amused.

With jokes and laughter that kept them going over the two miles of snow-deep road, they reached their new home. The younger children followed in the farm wagon buttressed about with the mattresses. Then, on Christmas Eve, Mother Du-

Mother Duchesne filled her apron with corn.

chesne and Mother Audé left the farm with one of the cows in the early morning.

"It's so cold I can scarcely walk!" said Mother Audé, watching while Mother Duchesne tugged at the rope fastened round the neck of the cow. "I expect that's the matter with Blanchette. Perhaps she'll follow if we go on. Set her loose, Mother."

Mother Duchesne filled her apron with corn. Blanchette took a few bites and stood twisting her jaws appreciatively. Mother Audé unfastened the rope. Blanchette suddenly sprang into life and rushed off into the field.

"She'll get lost in a drift!" cried Mother Duchesne, and the two of them gave chase, stumbling through the thick piles of snow hiding bushes that tore their habits and veils, tripping and sinking deep into drifts.

"We'll never get her," said Mother Audé, teeth chattering in spite of her exertions.

"Let her go," said Mother Duchesne. With frozen fingers she was trying to pick up the things she had dropped. "All our money and papers and my watch have fallen into the drift here, and the snow has blown inside my gloves and I can't feel anything."

Mother Audé retrieved the lost property but by that time Blanchette had gone peacefully back to the farm and they went on without her.

By midday they had reached the convent. The children welcomed them with laughter and delight.

"It's a marvellous place!" they cried. "There's a downstairs and two upstairs storeys! There'll be proper classrooms and Mother Berthold says the big room we'll use as a dormitory can be a study room in the daytime just like the ones in France. And the chapel's inside the house, too, so that we'll be under the same roof as Our Lord."

"The kitchen is grand!" said Sister Manteau. "With a proper stove and bake-oven, I'll be able to do my best for the children."

"Do you know," said Sister Lamarre, "they've actually got the well inside the house... And there's a cellar we can store things in."

Mother Duchesne laughed at their pleasure. Yet what a tiny place it was, in all conscience, and how heavily the debts for its building hung upon her! Would they ever get the forty boarders that would make them self-supporting? At the Midnight Mass, she thought of the Stable Cave of Bethlehem and the choice that God had made for His life on earth.

"I do not mind poverty, as far as I am concerned," she reflected. "A true, humbling and despised sort of poverty is most like that of Our Lord, and I welcome it as a gift from His Sacred Heart. But debts—they harass the soul."

Mother Barat had written in distress: "Your bishop has asked me now for fifteen thousand francs and five more religious—I have neither to give."

Even she did not realize fully the penury in which her daughters lived since they did not dwell on it in their letters. How could they ask for more when they knew the troubles that pressed her on all sides?

Spring came to Florissant with green bursting buds on the forest trees and the frozen creeks on each side of the convent ran again through meadows bright with blossom. There was a large oil painting of St Francis Regis in the chapel now. The bishop had unexpectedly found it in a case of pictures sent him from Rome and had given it in fulfilment of a grateful promise made when Mother Duchesne won him a favour from the saint. There was a piano, too, in the parlour. It had come in its packing case all the way from France—the children of Grenoble, Paris, and Beauvais had sent it, and now the children of Missouri trained their fingers with scales and exercises, and picked out tunes with care. Perhaps it played no unimportant part in raising the number of boarders to twenty-two by the end of May. It gave dignified tone to all the school gatherings. It helped to keep alive the gay, singing happiness of the children. The melodies of the Old World brought something of its ancient living soul to the New, and helped to soften the pioneering crudities of a vigorous young nation.

"How lonely Mother Duchesne must be!" thought Mother Berthold one day, with the insight that love gives. "We can all go to her with our troubles, but she has no one to turn to. Mgr Dubourg—kind as he is, she can't speak freely to him. He doesn't fully understand us. Three times now he has wanted us to change our rule, though our only strength lies in our being 'one heart and one soul in the Heart of Jesus.' He takes her steadfastness for rigidity. He told her when she spoke to Americans, she had not the suavity of St Francis of Sales, though I should like to know how suave the Bishop of Geneva would have been if he had tried to express himself in English. Fr Richard at St Charles saw further, but he wasn't really a kindred soul. Fr de la Croix meets her on the field of valiant self-denying labour but he's not her equal in prayer, and the Trappist Father has gone from here before we got to know him. If only Fr de Andreis was not ill!"

Her thoughts went back to the autumn when the bishop had brought them this saintly Italian Lazarist to be their chaplain while Fr de la Croix was away among the Indians. She remembered the day when they had all been talking together and the bishop had praised the singing of the children.

"The nuns have taught them so many lovely motets," he said, and turned to her. "Mother Berthold, will you not sing us that hymn to Our Lady we had at my Mass last week?"

It was one of Fr Barat's composing. Simply, she had begun to sing. The young priest had listened to her opening notes intently. Then she had seen him suddenly flush, grow pale, cling to his chair, and then kneel, while tears flowed down his cheeks and his closed eyes seemed fixed on some inward vision that took him far from the smiling valley of Florissant and the voice of a poor nun. She had finished her hymn, and the bishop had talked of this and that until Fr de Andreis had returned to the everyday world. When the two had left them, Mother Duchesne was radiant, too.

"Do you remember the ecstasy of St John of the Cross when St Teresa's nuns sang to him?" she had asked.

Mother Berthold had thought, "How little one knows the consequences of one's doings! Fr Barat could never have guessed that what he penned so long ago would in so distant a land have given a saint a glimpse of heaven. I was only an instrument. But perhaps one has to be in the community of a saint if the song is to do its work."

Saints understood saints. Fr de Andreis and Mother Duchesne spoke the same language of the soul. He could give her the spiritual companionship she needed. He had given them a retreat. He had promised to return. But his work had not yet permitted it, and ill health was dogging him. Mother Berthold remembered his words. "We must follow Divine Providence, step by step, without ever interrupting, anticipating, or deserting it." Divine Providence seemed now to want Mother Duchesne to be alone. Mother Berthold sighed because all she could offer was loyal love. Perhaps that was something.

But God balanced hardships with graces. On 19 August, Mary Layton arrived from Barrens with her parish priest, Fr Rosati, to ask admission to the Society.

"I've no education," she said. "I couldn't teach and I don't wish to try, but I want to serve Our Lord. May I enter as a sister?"

Mother Duchesne accepted her.

"You speak no French; I speak only bad English," she warned Mary Layton. "You will find it hard to understand me."

"I don't mind," said the postulant. She could always ask Mother Berthold to explain the practical things. The holiness of her superior she could understand quite well by herself.

Then in September, Mother Duchesne fell ill. A kind of erysipelas covered her body and she burned with fever. The remedies given her seemed only to increase her sufferings and her headaches made her delirious. The doctor counselled the Last Sacraments as he held out no hope.

As she lay on her mattress on the floor, Mother Duchesne looked back over her life, and saw herself facing her Maker and her Judge with empty hands. With all she might have done, she had only failures to offer. Others desired and accomplished: she was left with barren wishes. She thought of Fr de Andreis at work among the Indians, longing, like her, to go beyond the Rockies to China and to labour there, too. He was young. His ill health would yield to treatment, and he would go. But she would never see almond-eyed yellow children to win for Christ; she would never roam among the Rockies in search of Redskins. How they were calling her! The mountains were all about her now, but she could not find the trail of the children. The peaks reared up, snow-capped and glacial. There were streams descending through pine woods, flowing together into a river that moved swiftly under a bridge between houses, and there was a convent on a hill. Of course, these were the mountains of Dauphiné. It was not she who was dying, but Aloysia Jouve: Aloysia who lay racked with pain. She must find something to cure her. Aloysia was going to China. Aloysia would find the lost Redskin children in the Rockies. She would meet Fr de Andreis. They were both young. They both had work before them. They would not have to meet God with empty hands. No, it was she herself, after all, who was dying. Empty-handed. An unprofitable servant, with nothing done in her fifty-two years of life.

Though she did not know it, on a lonely Atlantic island, understanding now that his complaint was beyond cure, Napoleon Bonaparte, too, was summoning his forces to face the Last Enemy.

Mother Audé wrote in haste to the bishop to tell him of the sorrow that was overwhelming them. At once he rode back to them, bringing with him the best doctor of St Louis. A skilful treatment began to revive hopes. The bishop said Mass the next morning in honour of St Francis Regis. By the week's end, Mother Duchesne was out of danger.

"Fees?" asked the young doctor when the bishop approached

him. "Tell them I'll not take a penny over and above the cost of the medicines, and I'll be honoured to attend them at any time. My Lord, it does me good to see so much charity and devoted work, and all with such poverty. I've got to get to heaven, too."

At the end of October, when Mother Duchesne was convalescent, news was brought them that Fr de Andreis had died. Before the tabernacle, Mother Duchesne remembered the words he had spoken in the autumn: "God alone is great, and happy is the man who lives only for Him."

"I have been yearning for someone to lean on. Now I must lean upon God and on Him alone," she thought.

Mother Duchesne was well enough to take her part in Mary Layton's clothing on 22 November. She wrote in her Journal: "On this happy day those of the pupils who have a talent for music sang the Mass, and very well, too. The altar was still adorned with the decorations of yesterday, the feast of the Presentation in the Temple. We took advantage of this to celebrate in a becoming manner the first religious clothing that has taken place in Upper Louisiana since the beginning of the world, and great was our joy to see another soul entirely consecrated to the Sacred Heart."

The first novice of the Sacred Heart in the New World tucked up her habit when the ceremony breakfast was over, put a shawl round her shoulders and went out to see to the cows. They could not wait while she said lengthy prayers in the chapel. But it did not matter. Christ went with her to the cowshed. Nothing could separate her from His love.

The winter was severe. Sister Layton cheerfully broke the frozen milk with hammer and knife, and radiated warm-heartedness. Mary Ann Summers, who had been given a home by Mother Duchesne when her parents died, watched and envied, and offered to join her. Other eyes among the boarding-school pupils watched appraisingly and counted costs. Fifteen-year-old Emilie St Cyr was not blind to the price the choir nuns were paying for their education. She asked to be one of their company. On 19 March there were two more white veils at work in the convent.

Then the mail arrived from France, and they learnt that Aloysia Jouve had died. At Grenoble, her going from them on 21 January had been that of another St Agnes, virgin and martyr, and those who came to say a prayer beside her as she lay smiling in death sensed the outpouring of graces from the Church Triumphant. Her younger sister, Amélie Jouve, realized now what Aloysia had meant when she said, "You will replace me." With their younger sister, Constance, she asked to be a novice. Her brother Henri, careless and scarce believing, recognized with unclouded mind the true worth of life and decided to be a Jesuit. Josette de Saussure, who had asked her father to accompany her, saw the tears in his eyes. As they went back down the hill, he said, "I am a romantic, Josette. I lived unmoved by the grandeur of the epic, but this perfect lyric has touched my heart."

There were cures of body, as well as of soul.

"The other nuns will give you an account of the miracles being wrought through her intercession. What a consolation for you!" wrote Mother Barat, her heart torn between grief and joyful triumph. She had dreamed that all her daughters should be like Aloysia.

"At the age of twenty, full of strength, of energy, of facility, of zeal, Aloysia believed she was destined for the appealing missions of Louisiana," wrote the convent chronicler at Ste Marie's, "but in the designs of God, she was to become their zealous protector in heaven."

Eulalia and Mathilda Hamilton, who had finished school, asked to enter the society. Mother Duchesne felt that her niece was sending her this consolation.

"She has left me far behind, both as to virtue and its reward," she thought. "Her short life filled to the brim—and mine so worthless, so many graces abused, and so imperfect still. Perhaps her merits will hide my defects. What is St Francis Regis doing that he allows St Aloysius to get ahead of him in giving graces of sanctification? At least I have the privilege of belonging to the Society of Our Lord's Sacred Heart, to which I gave Aloysia."

She did not repine over the loss of Aloysia to the missions on earth. God's ways were always best.

On 6 May Napoleon Bonaparte died on St Helena. The Emperor of France had looked back on his life and seen the day of his First Communion as the happiest of his life. Now at the end he accepted grace and met death as a child of God, looking forward to eternal happiness.

But by that time, Mother Duchesne was again milking the cows, digging in the garden, teaching French to the senior girls, and spending long vigils in prayer when the multifarious tasks of superior were accomplished.

"We are learning by experience that happiness can be allied to very much pain," said Mother Duchesne.

There was plenty of pain in the thought of her failure to make a success of the boarding school, but the bishop had begun in the summer of 1821 to build a new church next to it, a church he would never have planned had the convent not been there. He was dedicating it to the Sacred Heart, the first church so dedicated west of the Mississippi. Mother Barat had said as they set off from Paris, "If you only establish one new tabernacle in Louisiana, ought you not to consider yourselves greatly blest?"

There was another kind of pain in the new plan the bishop had proposed and the Mother General accepted, now that American vocations gave promise for the future. At Grand Coteau in the south, a wealthy widow offered house, lands, and slaves for the foundation of a school for girls. The bishop had offered her the nuns of the Sacred Heart. The time had come for the little band to break the ties that the shared joys and sorrows, labours and graces of four years had drawn so close. Mother Duchesne's deeply loving heart felt the sacrifice. She would give the best she had that the new enterprise should prosper. She offered Mother Audé as superior, gracious, tact-

P

ful, competent Mother Audé whom children and parents loved so well. On 5 August 1821, when the dew was still on the meadow grass, Mother Audé and Sister Layton drove away. The Society was growing. It had been sown in tears, but God was giving at length the increase.

"As for me," Mother Duchesne wrote to Mother Barat, "put me where you wish. All my desires save that of doing God's Will are extinguished."

25: Low Waters

IT was three o'clock, and the warm August sky seen through the patterning of forest branches had not yet lightened with the coming of day. The ox-cart creaked and jolted, and the driver's exhortations to his long-haired beasts wove themselves into a rhythmic refrain till "Flambeau, Gaillard, Rousseau, et Tout Blanc" was a melody that matched the swaying lantern. But it was not that their journey had begun at two in the morning and was leading them through woods and marshlands as fantastic as fairy-tales that kept Thérèse Pratte awake and set her heart dancing. It was because each step the oxen took was bringing her nearer to her loved Mother Audé. That was something so unbelievably, unexpectedly true, that she could not have slept a moment. Moments were too precious in their joyous anticipation to be wasted in sleep. She looked round at her companions in the ox-cart. They were reminders of all the happy chain of things that had led to this day. The two novices had slipped together along the bench and their tired heads rested against the side of the cart in unconcerned sleep. Mother Emilie St Cyr—she had been in the school only last year, and now she was part of the Society that held Mother Audé. But it was not just Mother Audé that attracted people—Cousin Emilie Chouteau had run away from home in a cart driven by a negro workman and would have shared the hard life with Mother Duchesne at Florissant—only

Mother Duchesne had sent her back to her family. Mother Duchesne was kind—but in a different way from Mother Audé. She was awake now, Thérèse knew, watching lest Sister Mullanphy slipped off her bench, and praying.

When Mother Mathevon arrived from France in April, Mother Duchesne had glowed—Thérèse had known how happy they both were to meet again. Mother Mathevon had told her then of the French house they had lived in together up in the mountains—mountains that made them both long for the Rockies and the souls of Redskins, so of course they were happy to be together once more, but Mother Duchesne wasn't one to keep her happiness to herself. Mother Murphy had come from France, too, and was at Grand Coteau, yet Mother Audé's community had been ill, and she wanted more assistance. That was why Mother St Cyr and Sister Mullanphy were here in the cart, ready to join the two Southern novices, Mother Gérard and Sister Landry; that was why Mother Duchesne had come herself to help as no one else could; and she, Thérèse Pratte, was there because Mother Duchesne had known how she would glow if she saw Mother Audé again, and had asked her father if she might come to be her companion there and back again. Of course, her father had consented. It was an education to go the thousand and more miles down the Mississippi. She would be learning other things than geography, too.

They set off on Saturday, 20 July. They had hoped to hear Mass the next day at Ste Geneviève but the captain was still unloading at Herculaneum. Thérèse saw how it grieved Mother Duchesne to be deprived of Mass, but she had said, "Well, Thérèse, it is the Will of God," and had taken her for a walk along the river bank. Two little girls and a barking dog had followed them in curiosity. Their father had come up and asked if they were Catholics. His eldest child was baptized, but not the youngest. A priest who was on the steamer came at Mother Duchesne's request, and there was a baptism, then and there, and Thérèse was the godmother. She felt almost like a missioner herself, now, with the responsibility of mothering a soul. It was queer how God had used the loading of a steamer to give that grace.

She had been like one of a great united family when they had all been to Mass for their Mother General on St Mary Magdalen's feast day, and Mother Duchesne had told them tales of Mother Barat. The journey was all so interesting—the little wooden church that was too large for the careless Catholics at Natchez, the crowds that were going into the Presbyterian church, the priest who sang their evening hymn with them on the steamer, the inn at Plaquemine where the spiders were better lodged than the travellers, the flat-boat voyage along the bayou, the black waters under the dense woods, the romantic possibility of a night lost in the marsh far from land with only a bit of bread to keep them from starvation, the excitement of pursuit by a boat-load of cannibals who turned out after all to be good-natured Indians and negroes anxious to put them on their right way, and finally, the ox-cart waiting in the mud on shore to take them to an inn for a short rest until they set out again at two. Yes, it was interesting, but the best was still to come. With the rising sun, they left behind the marshland and jogged along by cotton fields where the black children in the midst of the snow-like plants raised smiling faces to watch them pass. Then the driver pulled up.

"There you are," he said, pointing to a clump of live-oaks and pines. "There's the convent."

They clambered out and set off through the garden. A man at work there looked up, and made for the house. The door stood open. Thérèse had no eyes for the crowd of children thronging within, or the three unknown nuns who had appeared at the man's call as if by magic. All she saw was Mother Audé who came running out, the tears of joy streaming from her eyes while she cried, "Mother! Mother!" and threw herself into the arms of Mother Duchesne. Then everybody seemed to laugh and cry and embrace each other while the children in the background wondered and stood on tiptoe and laughed too. Then Mother Duchesne pulled her forward and she was in

Mother Audé's arms and it would have been worth going twice the length of the journey to find how dear she still was and how unforgotten.

"Why, you've grown!" Mother Audé said. "But of course you're fifteen now. It's the last day of term, so you'll see some of the school."

That evening, they would give a reception for Mother Duchesne, just as if they were French children at Ste Marie's. Mother Murphy took the seventeen girls and saw to it that their curtseys should be as graceful as any in Paris. Mother Audé wrote out an address in elegant French and looked round for the best person to read it.

"Mary Ann Hardey, don't you think?" suggested Mother Murphy. "She's not in the top class, but she won't get nervous and spoil it all."

They cleared the desks from the study room and put down a carpet at one end, with a chair of honour in the middle flanked by ordinary chairs for the other nuns. The girls sat round in a semi-circle. The hour struck; Mother Duchesne entered and took her place. Mary Ann Hardey rose, curtseyed faultlessly, then read her address.

"Good, good!" thought Mother Murphy. "It sounds like any French girl!"

Mother Duchesne listened attentively, looking at the girl's serious face and her golden hair. When Mary Ann raised her blue eyes, it was as if another Aloysia was speaking to her. She smiled when the address was over, thinking of past and present, and when the other nuns left her alone with the school, she knew that the past in France and the present in America had made one. Mary Ann Hardey, lost now in the group, was thinking of the future. This was another of the nuns she had begun to venerate. She had watched Mother Audé carefully, she had noted Mother Murphy's unruffled cheerfulness, and Sister Layton's devotedness. She had seen Carmélite Landry and Mother Gérard become daily more like them. What others had done, she could do. She would want to be a saint, too, full of

mortification and zeal, like St Aloysius, winning an early crown
in youthful holiness, like Mother Audé or Mother Murphy.
But this nun was somehow different. Her tired blue eyes
seemed to have seen sadder things that made the kind lines on
her face quieter and stronger. Mary Ann felt she would understand a great many things and stand firm in times of trouble.
She doubted whether she would ever get that kind of holiness.

The next day, 8 August, the school children went away for
their fortnight's holiday. Mother Duchesne took charge. The
invalids were given proper rest, the business affairs talked over,
the recreations made joyful and souls restored by a retreat.

"I shall have to read the instructions to you, as we can't get
a priest," she said, apologetically, and gave herself without
stint to them. Mother Murphy was enchanted. She wrote to
Mother Barat, "I wanted someone to speak to, someone to
whom I could open my heart . . . I have never been able to
speak to any one with more facility and never felt greater peace
than in accepting Mother Duchesne's decision."

Mother Duchesne was full of admiration at what her
daughters had done. She had always known Mother Audé
would succeed where her own lack of holiness caused failure.
She wrote with joy to tell Mother Barat that the school was
growing and that many girls who arrived untrained and wild
had already been transformed. Thank God there were these
young ones to do His work. Truly the bishop had called her an
old sinner. The twenty-ninth of August would be her fifty-
third birthday.

There was no Mass that day. She passed the whole of it at
the foot of the sanctuary. If Christ withheld the gift of Himself
from His worthless servant, she would yet give Him herself in
all her worthlessness.

That same day Mother Murphy was writing in her journal,
"May her valuable life be long, long preserved. May she live to
see her children and her children's children peacefully established in Louisiana," and Mary Ann Hardey, back at school,
was watching, and listening, and learning from Mother Du-

chesne's explanation of the school rule how to be a child of the Sacred Heart.

Thérèse Pratte knew that there would come an end to the happiness of seeing Mother Audé. On 2 September there were tears in all eyes as she climbed into the cart that was to take Mother Duchesne away. She was in tears herself but Mother Duchesne was cheering the disconsolate group of nuns and smiling her loving farewells.

"God alone," she said as she took her place beside Thérèse, and the driver flicked at his two horses. They were off now down the road that led across the sunny prairie-land to the dark cypress woods. The horses' canter slowed down to a walk. Mother Duchesne saw Thérèse's tears and pointed to the horses.

"That skinny one on the off-side belongs to the convent," she said. "He makes me think of the Pale Horse of the Apocalypse."

Thérèse dried her eyes to look. He certainly was not a blood horse nor was his pair a thoroughbred. They had reached the dark shade of the wood. Trees with a thick mantle of Spanish moss kept out the sun, and the road ran through marshy land. The air was clammy, Thérèse felt, as though they had left behind all that was bright and fresh. The apocalyptic horse evidently felt the same. He stopped short, bringing his companion to a standstill. The driver urged, cajoled, and used his whip. Nothing would make him move forward.

"We'll get out," Mother Duchesne suggested, and they dismounted. The horses started forward suddenly. Kicking, rearing and plunging, with the driver vainly trying to hold them in, they jerked the cart forwards and sideways and landed at length knee-deep in the thick mud of a quagmire. The man stood stupidly by the road. This was the end.

"Come along, Thérèse," said Mother Duchesne. "Let's see if we can move them."

The horses seemed docile now, but powerless to pull the cart out. A negro came by and stopped to laugh. Good-naturedly he helped unharness the horses and unload the cart. Then he pulled to some purpose and they had their chariot again. But at the next inn, they found oxen to draw them to the landing stage of the bayou boat.

The water had become even lower since their outgoing journey. Under the huge cypresses, twisted and gnarled, it ran black and fetid. The streamers of moss hanging from the dark branches swayed lifelessly over patches of yellow decaying foliage. There were stagnant pools covered with green slime, and when they passed places where water-lilies grew luxuriantly, Mother Duchesne thought that their bright pink or white or gold blossoms threw into deeper relief the treacherous black waters below. Only the myriads of mosquitoes rising and circling above the muddy streams had life. The dip of the boatmen's oars broke into a silence that seemed to be listening only for the croaking of bull-frogs or the harsh cry of cranes. It was a relief to come to the deeper part of the bayou and to transfer to the bayou steamer that took them to Plaquemine.

"You'll have to wait for a steamer up the river," said the surly innkeeper there. "And you'll be lucky if one stops here. We're none so keen to have them put in here. They say there's yellow fever in New Orleans, and we don't want it."

They waited without avail for five days. Thérèse felt she knew every spider's web that festooned the dismal inn. There did not seem any other way of escape than going to the city.

At New Orleans, the Ursulines received them with joy.

"You are not well," said the Reverend Mother, appraising Mother Duchesne's tired look, and called for the doctor. He shook his head.

"If she stays any longer in this place," he said, "she runs the risk of catching yellow fever. My advice is, go north by the first possible steamer."

Weary as she was, Mother Duchesne took her way to the landing stage with Thérèse. How different were the thoughts that now filled her mind from the forward-looking hopes and fears of four years before! She had measured now the difficulty of the task before her, and had plumbed her own insufficiency. But she must take to herself what she told others. God alone mattered.

"Mother, there's the *Hecla*," Thérèse pointed out. It was on the point of starting, black smoke streaming from its funnel. As she followed the girl down the gangway, Mother Duchesne paused. A horror seized her as though her step down on to the deck was a step into a newly dug grave. There was noise and laughter coming from the saloon, there were passengers leaning along the side of the boat, there were sailors busy about their tasks; yet behind it all, the Pale Horse waited with its rider. She went forward to the ladies' quarters, feeling chilled, though the heat lay heavy over city and river as the *Hecla* started upstream.

The next day the second mate was in charge of the steamer. "Where's the captain?" asked one of the passengers.

"Dead," said the second mate laconically, and added, "The first mate's gone, too. It's the yellow fever."

A passenger died that day. Another was in such agonies of pain that they put him on shore and left him to die on the outskirts of a village. Mother Duchesne knew now that she, too, had the fatal yellow fever.

"You must keep away from me, and in the open," she ordered Thérèse. There were others stricken, and dying like animals, while those who had escaped drank and joked and sang without a care for them. She saw one man in a corner, groaning and cursing, shunned by all. She summoned all her strength and went to him, moving him to a more comfortable position, moistening his feverish lips. He looked at her, surprised at her gentleness, and then turned his head from her with a despairing groan. He did not want to die. Death was the end of all. She came to him again, though it cost her to move and to speak. He must not die like a dog. She spoke to him very simply of God, of His love, of redemption through Jesus Christ, of eternal life in the blessedness of the Triune God. He grasped at what she said.

"I've never had any religion," he murmured. "I wish I had yours. Can't I be baptized?"

"If you believe with all your heart, you can," said Philippine.

The man looked at her. She had told him she belonged to the Sacred Heart of Jesus. She had been kind to him.

"I believe Jesus is God," he said.

She rose and went in search of a basin. The man behind the bar in the saloon filled it for her from the muddy Mississippi and gave her the glass she asked for. Groups of men playing cards looked up at her through clouds of tobacco smoke and, finding her uninteresting, continued their game. Out again on the deck she knelt beside the dying man and baptized him. A rowdy song arose from the *Hecla* and insulted the majesty of the Father of Waters. The rider on the Pale Horse waited; but one man on that ill-fated boat was caught up by the Horseman on the White Horse, to whom a crown has been given and who rides out victorious.

When the man was dead, Mother Duchesne could no longer hide her own illness.

"Put her on shore," some of the passengers complained, keeping their distance. "It's not fair on us to have her on board."

"I'm coming with you," said Thérèse fiercely. She had seen what heroic charity was. It would be much better to die with Mother Duchesne than live with the *Hecla's* passengers.

One of the men came forward.

"I'm going ashore and I'll put you on your way to lodgings," he said.

They landed at Natchez, but at the entrance to the town they were stopped. No one from New Orleans might enter for fear of contagion.

"We'll try the other bank," said the man, and he led the way back and bargained with a boatman to ferry them across.

"You stay with the lady here," he said to Thérèse. "I'll go ahead and see what I can get."

Seated on the hot sand of the river bank, Mother Duchesne burnt with fever. How blessed it would be to die and leave to others the anguishing task of winning souls! Blessed? To die without Sacraments? To go alone on her last journey, to face her Judge alone? Besides, she must watch over Thérèse. That was her duty—the duty that was God's Will.

"Well, I've got you in somewhere!" The man had returned pleased and yet ill pleased. "There's a man whose wife died three weeks ago—a funny customer—but he'll take you. He told me you could have his wife's bed. It's just as it was when she died. It's the house up the road there. Your young lady can have another room."

He went off. Mother Duchesne rose and slowly walked to the house. She must not let Thérèse see what it cost her. Once within the room, she sat straight up though the fever had reached its height.

"I shall be all right," she said. "You need not see after me."

She shut herself in, avoiding the bed and its soiled sheets. Alone, she fought the weakness that urged her to let go of everything, and the fever that gave no cool respite. Alone for four days she struggled against death, and on the fifth she felt the fever lessening. She longed now with an intense longing for the Sacraments. Thérèse could get a message across to the priest at Natchez. She would be ready to die then. But the priest could not come. He could give help to her body, but not to her soul. He arranged for two good Catholics to take her into their house and nurse her. At the end of a few weeks she had recovered.

"Oh, Mother, it's good to see you well again!" said Thérèse. She had learnt now not to be afraid of her. She could not take liberties with Mother Duchesne, but she could show her simply how much she loved her.

When the steamer *Cincinnati* put in to Natchez, they boarded her. There were quiet days of travel upstream, with only the clanging danger bell to disturb them. They stopped at

the junction of the Mississippi and the Ohio and went on shore
while the boat unloaded.

"Look there!" said Thérèse, pointing to a boat pulled up on
its side on the shore. "There's a wrecked steamer."

They drew nearer.

"Why, it's the *Hecla*!" cried Thérèse.

There were three men sitting by the hulk, gloomily con-
templating a gaping hole in her side. One was the second
officer, who recognized them and came towards them.

"The voyage was hell," he said. "The boiler burst—two of
the men were burnt so as their own mothers wouldn't know
them—and the yellow fever! Do you see the island yonder in
midstream? We buried thirteen there. Thirteen! Ah, the voyage was unlucky!"

Mother Duchesne was very silent as they walked back.

"God's sheltering arm has protected us," she said at length
to Thérèse.

"I'm glad I'm travelling with a saint," thought the girl. "It
might be quieter and more peaceful with ordinary people, but
it's safer with a holy one."

At New Madrid, a hundred miles from St Louis, the *Cincinnati* ran on to a sandbank.

"We're stuck here till the river rises," said the captain, "and
that won't be till the winter rains begin, I guess."

"Thérèse," said Mother Duchesne, "I think you will find
enough to amuse yourself while we wait. You can talk to the
other passengers in English. I can't, and none of them speak
French, so I shall make my retreat." She thought, "Alone with
God in the midst of a crowd! How I long for Mass and Communion! Even if we start soon, I shall have been sixty days
without spiritual food. I never fasted for so long during the
Revolution. I must have God at all costs. There is a Bible in the
cabin. I have my Office Book. I must avail myself of this
opportunity."

Thérèse found Catholic friends in the neighbourhood. Mr
and Mrs Kay asked them to accept hospitality while they

waited for the steamer. Listening to the girl's talk, they felt they were going to entertain a saint. Seeing Mother Duchesne, they were even more sure.

"But saints sometimes have an outside that stops people getting any further," said Mrs Kay in private to her husband. "I can see plenty of us Americans being put off by her French manners."

"The bark of the tree," said her husband. "A trifle hard to penetrate. But it's heart of oak within."

On the fifth day of their stay, the heavens opened and torrential rain fell. The Mississippi rose unexpectedly and the *Cincinnati* floated off the sandbar. By 28 November they had reached St Louis. Thérèse went home while Mother Duchesne set off for Florissant.

"I'm glad you went, in spite of everything," said Mr Pratte when the story had been told.

"It's been the greatest grace of my life," said Thérèse. She knew now what life meant. She had learnt its value.

At Florissant, Mother Berthold, Mother Mathevon, Sister Manteau, Sister Lamarre, and the two Hamilton novices were sitting round their Superior with hearts overflowing with love and gratitude. Nothing mattered now that their Mother was back. To-morrow there would be troubles to tell her of, but to-night there was only a joy too deep for words.

26: Ebb and Flow

THE man folded up the bank notes and put the wad into his breast pocket. "Well, seeing as you've cleared the account, I'll take back what I said about Catholics never paying their bills," he remarked grudgingly. "But it's what they're saying right and left in the city. The bishop'll be lucky if they don't sell him up—running into debt to a pretty tune—and the Catholics are sick of him, too. You won't expect any more groceries from me, madam. I can't afford to let it be known I supply the convent. There's two of your old pupils going about St Louis saying you poison the children. It's not a good advertisement for my goods."

He climbed into his cart and drove off. Mother Duchesne thought, "God's providence that he came to-day when I received Mme de Rollin's money from Grenoble. What would he have said if I had offered him the last six sous I had yesterday? But he's not the only one. These debts are crushing me."

Mother Berthold came to her.

"Don't blame yourself, Mother," she urged. "They are saying all kinds of things against us in St Louis—if the bishop had not removed to New Orleans, it would be against him that they would be speaking."

"Well, thank God it's upon poor women like us that the attacks are made," said Mother Duchesne. "Far better than that the head of religion should be insulted."

"It's a queer country," said Octavie Berthold, daughter of the secretary of M. Voltaire. "I suppose that is what they mean by freedom of speech. Long live the rights of man—they keep slaves, and are dispossessing the Indians. It's a land of plenty and of penury. These pioneering families put up with conditions that would surprise us in France, but it's not for love of poverty. Soon they'll want more comfort than we could dream of."

There was a clatter of hoofs along the road, and they saw a carriage stop. The negro driver hitched the horse to a post and opened the door for the gentleman within. As he alighted, the door slipped from the negro's grasp and swung to against the master's arm. They heard his loud exclamation of anger, the deprecatory tones of the negro; then the white man's arm was raised in a swift gesture and his hand struck full across the slave's face. He fell back, both hands to his face, while his master pursued his way up to the convent door. Mother Duchesne passed him in a flash, but he did not heed her. It was with Mother Berthold, who spoke English, that his business lay.

The negro was seated on the ground, his face hidden against his knees, while his body swayed to and fro. Mother Duchesne raised one of his great black hands and kissed it. That was a language he could understand. He looked at her while a trickle of blood ran down from the weal where his master's ring had caught him, and he saw a deep compassion in her eyes. There was something else he did not grasp. How could he? He had never before met a white woman at his feet asking forgiveness for all the wrongs done to his race.

Mother Duchesne called to a novice at work in the garden.

"Bring a bowl of warm water," she said, and when it came she bathed the man's face herself and spread an ointment on the wound. When it was done, he kissed her hand. He was ready beside his horse as his master came out, and drove away again.

Mother Berthold drew near to her with a sigh.

"That was Mr Durrant," she said. "He's taking Honoria away from school—we're not fashionable enough for him.

That leaves us with just two children who pay their fees. We can't go on like this, Mother. There are the six orphans we're keeping now—"

"We shall go on keeping them so long as we've any potatoes and maize to share with them," said Mother Duchesne firmly. "Where else could they go? Our Lady will provide."

"Well, then," Mother Berthold went on, "send back home the boarding-school children who never pay either for board or tuition."

"No," said Mother Duchesne again. "Many would lose their faith if they left us. Better to keep them and deprive ourselves of everything."

"What good do we do them, after all?" Mother Berthold queried. "At St Louis, when they've left us, they lose themselves in a round of pleasure—balls, plays, romantic novels, idleness, gossip—how can they swim against the stream? God is so easily forgotten."

Mother Duchesne sighed.

"I spoil everything, Octavie," she said. "I have told Mother Barat I am not capable of advancing our work here. But she has said, 'Trust the Heart of Jesus. He will strengthen our weakness and repair our foolish mistakes.' He has His ways of using us. Look at the novices He has sent us."

They certainly were a chosen band, Mother Berthold thought. She knew how much Mother Duchesne's example counted in their cheerful acceptance of hardships and poverty, in their love of prayer and fulfilment of their rule. How could they fail to catch her deep trust in the Heart of Jesus, her loyalty to His little Society, her oneness in heart and soul with all its members?

Mother Duchesne looked at them and longed to give them a Jesuit to direct them. In France, Fr Barat had still his heart in the New World. How blessed it would be if he could come as their chaplain! Something might be done, too, to help her tepid soul towards holiness if she could speak at last to one who so easily understood her. With a sudden pang, she realized he

Q

was nearing sixty. Like herself, he was growing old. Perhaps his superiors would think him too old for a new venture. He wrote back to her: "Unless I am taken up and carried away by the hair of my head, like the prophet Habacuc, I have no hopes of crossing the ocean."

There was too much work for French Jesuits in France. That door was closed.

Frederick William of Nassau, King of the Netherlands, had no love of Jesuits. He could not feel safe while they were in his dominions. They must be suppressed. Fr Charles van Quickenborne was not the man to be moved from his purpose by the princes of this world. There was a ship leaving for New York. On to it he marched with Fr Timmerman, seven young novices, and three lay-brothers. They would find temporary shelter with their brethren at the college of Georgetown. After that, God would provide.

Bishop Dubourg was on his way south from Washington where he had seen the President and had obtained support for the establishment of missions among the Indian tribes of the Missouri and Upper Mississippi. It remained now to find priests. His huge diocese swallowed up all those he had already. By chance he heard of the Flemish band. He went to Georgetown and offered his farm at Florissant to be their headquarters from which they could organize the conversion of the Redskin tribes.

"I have no means to offer you at the moment," he explained. "I wanted to find funds before I sought for men, but the men have come before the funds. That's the way God defeats the plans of our poor human prudence. All the same, I don't know how I can feed you."

Fr van Quickenborne smiled slowly.

"We'll be satisfied to rely on Providence," he said. "These young men are excellent material. They won't mind having 'for the greater glory of God' as their sole riches and their only support."

"God has called and sent me these labourers," said Mgr

Dubourg, feeling the weight of the souls in his care. "He will not let them die of hunger."

Sister Lamarre came to Mother Duchesne on the first day of June 1823.

"You know, Mother, they've absolutely nothing up at the farm. It's just as bare as when we arrived, and far more dirty than when we left. The bishop's sent three negroes to help with clearing the land. I reckon they'll eat more than they'll ever plant. And they're expecting the Jesuits to arrive on the third and there'll be nothing at all for them."

"We must see about that," said Mother Duchesne. "We can send them some bedding and linen."

"They'll not have any chairs," said Sister Lamarre. "We could spare the ones in the community room."

Sister Manteau found pots and pans in the kitchen.

"They'll not have any food in the house when they arrive," she suggested.

"We must send them provisions, then," said Mother Duchesne. Mr Pratte had called the day before and left a gift for her charities. Young men had big appetites, however holy they were.

"At least they will be upon the hill," said Mother Mathevon, "and won't have their cellars flooded with every rising of the creeks."

"But they will have to come down here to the valley to say Mass," Mother Duchesne reminded her. The new church built next to the convent was the parish church. The bishop had said the Jesuits would serve it.

Fr van Quickenborne called to make his arrangements. Mother Duchesne offered him the parish school to live in until the log cabin was ready. He accepted without great enthusiasm. A little hardship would not hurt young men of the stamp of Peter de Smet or Peter Verhaegen.

"They are to become saints," he said, phlegmatically. He looked about him, appraising the convent and the superior.

"You have a new Calvary in the garden," he remarked.

"We put it up this summer," said Mother Duchesne. "We needed the reminder of greater sufferings than ours."

She, too, was appraising this stolid Fleming. He was younger than she, but he would help her to reach the holiness she must have if God was to use her as an instrument. He accepted the task. Not for anything would he let her know that he was writing about the consolation their presence gave him and the hopes for religion that he built on the example of their piety and holiness. For her, he decided, it must be "God alone".

As the summer drew to a close, more and more children were taken away. Fr van Quickenborne agreed with her when she laid the failure of the boarding school at the door of her lack of spiritual understanding. However, he could hardly accuse her of the hurricane that deluged the countryside, broke down the convent walls, and devastated the garden—all her labours of the summer planting gone. He had to urge his roan horse through water six feet deep to get to the church for Mass.

"You'll find it's often like this in the winter, Father," said Sister Lamarre, philosophically. "When the two creeks overflow, we're left on an island."

Mother Mathevon's new trousseau from France was cut up and adapted for the use of the Jesuit novices. Hers were the only things the nuns had that were not worn out.

"Well, we've had practice in adaptation already," said Mother Hamilton. Her habit had been made out of an old black cassock left behind by a priest. One of the novices wore a white veil that had been a pupil's summer dress. "And I like helping men who are going to be priests."

"I'd be happier cleaning the boots of these good missionaries," said Mother Mathevon, "than being Queen of France."

The cabin of the farm on the hill was abandoned for a log house the Jesuits built for their noviceship with their own labour. The farm was properly cared for now. The fields were dug and crops planted. Mother Duchesne watched the young men one day toiling in the sun and her heart went out to them.

She and Sister Lamarre put their heads together and prepared a meal that they could do justice to.

"It's dripping and Indian corn they live on," Sister Lamarre said sadly. She knew herself what short commons were. This time there would be a treat. They watched their messenger go up the road to the farm.

Two hours later the dishes came back untouched. Very red about the face, the novice who returned them delivered his Fr Rector's message: "Fr van Quickenborne does not want Mother Duchesne's alms."

The Fr Rector learnt with an inward satisfaction that the Mother Superior had accepted his rebuke in silence, and had humbly asked the young man to take back with him the cassocks she had been mending. He felt he was dealing with a prospective saint. She would stand hard blows.

There was always work to do. Early in the morning the few children left in the boarding school could see her in the garden, digging or planting or gathering in the fruit. On wash days, she would be there, hanging out the clothes and taking them in again, sprinkling them and folding them ready for the ironing. The youngest child ran out after her as soon as class was over and followed her along the potato rows, picking up the potatoes as she dug them, listening to her stories told in broken English, with no less eagerness than the ragged boys of Grenoble. Her face was reddened by the sun and her blue eyes had lost their intense colour, but the child knew she was beautiful with the beauty of kindness. Together they would go into the church for a little visit. They understood each other with few words. It was good to be together.

Peter de Smet liked being with her, too, though, as a good novice, he kept in the background.

"What snubs our holy Fr Rector administers!" he noted. "Thank God he's dealing with a humble soul. It would go badly with us if she resented it. Food and clothing would suffer. We owe her material things—but who can count the spiritual blessings her prayers and sufferings win for us?"

One of Mother Duchesne's novices had an inkling of the treasures she was earning for them. Walking quietly through the garden, she had come unexpectedly upon her superior. The hot sun blazed down and the soil between the cabbages was hard and dry. The hoe she had been using lay beside a pile of weeds, and Mother Duchesne was seated near by. Her worn hands with the knuckles swollen from toil held her rosary, and the beads slipped through her fingers without ceasing. There was weariness in every line of her bent back and shoulders, and from her closed eyes, great tears were running, silent and unchecked, down her cheeks. On tip-toe the novice crept away. She had seen what she should not have seen. At the Calvary in the garden she stopped to say a prayer. It seemed to her that the downcast eyes of the Saviour and His weary face were mirrored down there in the vegetable patch.

Fr Timmerman died, but the valiant Fr van Quickenborne carried on single-handed until Peter de Smet was ordained, the first of the chosen band. The Indians were getting to know the Jesuit Black Robes. Sometimes they appeared in Florissant looking for the help of the Catholic faith. An Iroquois family passed through, asking for baptism. Fr Rector administered it in the church next to the convent.

"You will be godmother to this little girl," he said, as Mother Duchesne finished the preparations. The child's brother of twelve would stand godfather. Imperturbable, dark-eyed, the child suffered the water to be poured over her forehead.

"I baptize thee, Mary . . ." said Fr van Quickenborne. Mother Duchesne looked down at a soul into which the life of grace had entered. The first fruits of the Nations? Was it not worth a lifetime of labour? Why could she not be satisfied with this? Why did her heart cry out at once, "More, dear Lord, more! Beyond lie the forests and the Rocky Mountains. Southward are the Redskins of Peru. Across the ocean are the islands of Japan and the yellow millions of China. More, dear Lord, more!"

Mgr Dubourg gave the Jesuits a school for Indian boys at Florissant. In a few months they had received what she had longed for for years. The boys arrived, some half-dozen or so from different tribes, wild, ragged, unspeakably dirty. Only women could wash and mend for them. Mother Duchesne did the work herself, happy to contribute something. People in St Louis might look down on her. For the sake of her savages, even complete contempt would be welcome.

One evening in the early April of 1825, the community was saying office. The sky was clear with the fresh colour of spring, and there seemed a stir of life abroad.

"*Populus eius et oves pascuae eius; introite portas eius in confessione, atria eius in hymnis: confitemini illi,*" Mother Berthold's choir chanted, and on Mother Duchesne's side the answering verse came, "*Laudate nomen eius quoniam suavis est Dominus, in aeternum misericordia eius.*"

Sister Lamarre entered the church and went across to Mother Duchesne.

"Fr Rector wants you outside," she whispered.

Mother Duchesne laid down her office book and followed her out. At the door stood Fr van Quickenborne with his great black cloak hanging from his shoulders. He looked with a half-smile at her.

"Mother, I've brought you something," he said, and threw back the folds of his cloak. There, beneath his sheltering arms, were two little Indian girls, looking like frightened roebuck at the tall woman in front of them.

"For me?" Mother Duchesne could scarcely believe her eyes.

"For you," said Fr van Quickenborne. "It's little use our training boys unless the girls are cared for. I leave them to you."

When the community filed out from office, Mother Duchesne was happily feeding two children who clung to her habit as a refuge against a strange world.

The Jesuits brought them more Indian girls as the weeks went by. It was a full-time task to look after them. Reluctantly,

Mother Duchesne handed them over to a young Irish-American nun who had just made her vows. They followed her about as she did her outdoor tasks in stables and poultry yard, happily calling her "mamma". But lesson time was different.

"Where are your children?" Mother Duchesne asked one day as she found Mother O'Connor standing alone at the hour of class.

There was a rustle in the branches of the trees. Bright eyes looked down on the two nuns from the shelter of the foliage.

"Squirrels!" said Mother O'Connor, "that's what my children are. You can't expect them to sit still and learn their ABC. It would be more to the point if I joined them in the trees."

Slowly they came down to earth and slipped on to the ground before their teacher. Impassively they listened to her lesson. She was a woman of the Great Spirit. She was good to them like the old nun who was walking back to the house.

Mother Duchesne turned to the pile of dirty clothes, and began wash day for her beloved little savages.

"Our work is at last beginning," she thought happily.

Mother Mathevon wrote to Mother Barat: "Pray that we shall have a great number of children and that at last all these poor Indians will know God."

In Washington the chiefs of the Six Nations had been putting their symbols as signatures to treaties with the white men. It mattered little to the astute framers of the treaties that the signatories had little idea of their contents, and less understanding of the terms which could drive them further and further to the west.

27: Cross Currents

MOTHER Duchesne looked at her letter before folding it and slipping it into the envelope addressed to Mother Barat.

"Ever since you expressed your desire," she read, "I have been spreading my nets, sounding the ground, trying to get someone interested in the matter. On all sides I have met with nothing but opposition, coldness, indifference."

She paused. Yes, that was the bare truth. The wish of her superior was the expression of God's Will for her. But God was not making it easy for her to carry it out. Mother Barat had again come back to her wise plan of 1818 and was urging her to make a foundation in St Louis. Things had changed in the last nine years: only the difficulties remained as seemingly insuperable. Opposition, coldness, indifference. That was no exaggeration. In 1827, St Louis was beginning to fulfil its promise of commercial importance, its population was growing, new houses were rising everywhere, houses that were American in structure, overshadowing the old French dwellings with their gabled roofs of pioneer days. St Louis had its Cathedral, for its three thousand Catholics, but their children had no free schools. It surely must be God's Will for the Society to go there. Why then the opposition, the coldness and indifference, unless through her fault? Mother Audé, Mother Murphy, Mother Mathevon—any other nun would have won people's hearts.

"I am daily becoming more ugly," she thought, and looked out of the window to where the road ran along to Florissant. "Even in the village here, they call me, in a friendly way, 'the old witch'."

She turned again to her reading:

"At last I applied directly to Mr Mullanphy asking him if among his numerous pieces of property there was one he could sell at a moderate price for a work of charity and zeal. He soon offered me a house built of brick. . ."

That would delight Mother Barat, whose generous heart warmed always to generosity. Mr Mullanphy had already given his daughter to the Society in Paris. Now again his gift was princely. Some twenty acres of farmland round the house were to be the nuns' property for nine hundred and ninety-nine years, and all on payment of one dollar. True there were conditions. The nuns were to provide also for twenty poor orphans, but when did charity fail to move Mother Barat? It would be a heavy burden, but she could almost hear the Mother General rallying her: "I have every confidence that God will help you to bear it."

She returned to the letter.

"I went to inspect the property. The situation is less smiling than that of Ste Marie d'en Haut at Grenoble, but resembles it slightly, being elevated, solitary, in a healthy locality overlooking the Mississippi and the city."

She put the letter inside the envelope, but her thoughts ran back. Ste Marie—the sun on the mountains—the soft voice and happy smile of Mother Barat—the spring days when the snows were melting and the birds bursting into song. Less smiling than Ste Marie. But Ste Marie had had grim winters and heartbreaks. How easily one forgot them when the brightness of a saint shone out! Please God the new house at St Louis would one day shelter a saint. That would make it worthwhile to go through the difficulties and gloom of its beginnings. She remembered how she had taken an orphan to bring a blessing on her work in Grenoble—it would be a twentyfold benediction here. As she sealed the envelope, Mother Mathevon came into the room with her merry smile.

"I've finished the book-keeping for this month," she said. "The accounts just balance. It's the load of potatoes Fr van Quickenborne sent down for the Indian children that's done it."

"He's been so good to us," said Mother Duchesne. "Corn and firewood—what should we have done for our little Indian girls without them? We must pray for the Jesuits, Lucille. They will be able to go after the Indians into the wilds."

Mother Mathevon sighed.

"I wish we could follow them, too, Mother. I'm thinking the Indian children's expenditure won't worry us for long. Their numbers are dwindling. It's queer how God seems bent on giving us quite other work from what we imagine is needed."

"Yes," Mother Duchesne answered, thinking of the projected boarding school in Mr Mullanphy's house. "I was planning to go back again to St Charles. Fr Rector has bought the Duquette estate, the Jesuits are building a church there, and they want us in the old house. And yet now Fr Niell in Paris has made Mother Barat believe they want us in St Louis. St Charles will have to wait."

"We should have been too well off there," said Mother Mathevon, remembering her accounts. "This is the sort of house for me and you—poor and unimportant."

"You're right," said Mother Duchesne. "Abject and poor. That is why I like it."

"Then you'll love St Louis, too!" cried Mother Mathevon, smiling into her eyes. Mother Duchesne laughed with her.

"It's a good thing we're moving in in May," she said. "We'll not miss the fire we can't afford."

Mother Mathevon turned away. She had suddenly realized what this new foundation would mean. Mother Duchesne would be going away from Florissant, and they would be left. How they would miss her! No warmth of Maytide weather would make up for the loss of the fire of her love. Florissant without Mother Duchesne was unthinkable.

"Mother!" she said with a note of pain in her voice. Mother Duchesne looked at her and understood.

"Profit by these moments of trial," she said, smiling at her bravely. "This is the time to make progress. I always remember the words a man of God quoted to me, 'Unless the grain of wheat fall to the ground and die, it remaineth alone—'"

"Dying isn't an easy process," Mother Mathevon whispered, "even if we are dying for Our Lord."

"He will tell you of all He will do for you," Mother Duchesne answered, "—and of the ornaments He presents to you—the Cross, the thorns, the bonds. Jewels of Calvary. Be brave. Others before us have worn them and exchanged them at the last for joys the heart of man cannot conceive."

"I wonder what the future holds for us," said Mother Mathevon.

"Does it matter?" asked Mother Duchesne. "Be ready for work without rest, for prayer without consolation, for infirmity without solace. Then you will really belong to Our Lord's Sacred Heart."

They put together as many things as the poverty of Florissant could spare. On 2 May they were piled into the cart, and Mother Duchesne set off with Mother O'Connor, Julie Coutermarche, the woman who would run their errands for them, and four little orphans. The horse jogged along comfortably as the sun rose higher, and not until the afternoon did they find themselves in St Louis. Down Main Street they went, the eyes of the little girls wide as they sat agog to see all the strange sights of a city—the shops, the paving stones, a passing barouche in which reclined two ladies with silk parasols, the grand cathedral and the large new houses.

"Changes!" grunted their driver over his shoulder. "When I was a lad, this was the Rue Principale. When my father was young, it was the Rue Royale. What'll it be when you youngsters are my age? Ah well, the road remains."

He flicked at the flies round his horse's ears. Mother Duchesne thought:

"Yes, the road remains. Nine years ago I came up this road to see Bishop Dubourg, hoping to found a convent here that could be our central house in America. We had nuns and resources for it then, and the people were ready to receive us. But the bishop would not have us. Now he has gone down the road, back to France, and there is no more opposition in that quarter. But though this new bishop wants us, I haven't the nuns or the money and people cold-shoulder us. Yes, Rue Principale or Main Street, the road remains the same, Rue Royale, the Royal Road of the Cross."

The road went uphill and the houses thinned out. There were fields now, and the woods were closing in. They came upon a large pond, with coloured washerwomen at work, slapping and banging the clothes on the stones at its edge. The driver pointed with his whip to where the stream drained out at the bottom, and fell away to the river.

"That's the short cut to your property," he said. "But there's no bridge across the Mill Creek. We'll have to go all round Chouteau's Pond. You'll have to have a bridge built there if people are to get out to you easy-like."

Mother Duchesne's heart sank. Bridge-building on top of all the other necessary expenses, and no reserves of money! Promise of free-school pupils, but no boarders as yet in sight! But still, what was it that Fr Varin had written to her? "How good God is! What great things He had done for our Society! And after so many prodigies of grace, how could we be wanting in faith and trust? Courage and confidence! That is our motto until death!"

The women by the water paused in their work, watching the horse and cart. One called out to them. Their driver shrugged his shoulders, not deigning an answer.

"What did she say?" asked Mother O'Connor.

The man answered gruffly. "They say there's a ghost in the Mullanphy's house. Don't you mind, Mother. I've heard that tale before. They all say in St Louis it's haunted. What I say is, it doesn't matter if it is with all you holy ladies going to live there. No ghost could stick it out. No, that'll be all right. What I wouldn't be so keen on are all the woods yonder. There are plenty of Indian good-for-nothings and white tramps and loafers there that'll not run away at the sight of holy water. You're a bit lonely-like out here, aren't you?"

At last they pulled up before the brick house that was to be their home. They unloaded their few chairs, pots and pans, crockery, and the bundles of bedding and carried them in. The driver lent a hand and soon the cart was empty. They watched him drive off in a cloud of dust as he whipped the horse along the hard earth road, then they turned and surveyed their own property.

"Twenty acres!" cried Mother O'Connor. "That's grand, even if it is at the edge of a wilderness."

"We'll be able to farm it," said Mother Duchesne, "and grow flowers, too. I shall begin to feel like a countess. Come along in and get busy."

There was the dormitory to arrange for the orphans. There were plans to be made for their classroom and for the prospective boarders' dormitories and study rooms. Mother Duchesne found the largest room in the place in the basement and chose it for the Chapel.

"It must have been the kitchen once," said Julie Coutermarche, while the children looked with awe at the big fireplace as they stood on the stairs peering in.

"There's plenty of floor space," Mother O'Connor commented, "but I can almost touch the ceiling with my hand."

"We shall have to excavate the floor," said Mother Duchesne, noting its dampness. "We'll floor it, too, and plaster the walls. The altar can go in front of the fireplace." She stopped. She remembered that their poverty was very real. "We haven't a ciborium, so we shall not be able yet awhile to have the Blessed Sacrament here."

Julie Coutermarche was craning to look out of the window.

"I can't see another house anywhere, Mother," she said. "We're going to be lonely."

"Yes," said Mother Duchesne, looking at the empty fireplace, "we shall be lonely."

When would they shelter their Lord?

"They'll be building houses out this way," Mother O'Connor suggested. "You see. St Louis is on the march. Before we know where we are, they'll be calling this the City House. There'll be chimney pots all round about."

They all began laughing at the queer idea, and a toad that had been slowly crawling along the wall, slipped down between two bricks.

At nightfall, they locked up, and spread out their bedding on the floor. The big house felt empty, and the shadows thrown by their candles stretched, tall and wavering, over the bare walls. Mother Duchesne had found a cubby-hole under the stairs; it was little more than a cupboard but she could sleep there and save a room. She blew out her light, listened for a moment to the quiet house, then pulled the cover over her shoulders and fell asleep.

She roused some hours later with a start, knowing that some heavy body had fallen. Quickly she was outside in the corridor. Moonlight was streaming through the windows and showing fantastic knobs and cornices in the woodwork of the unfurnished house. She listened while a board creaked here and there, and a scurrying mouse ran behind the wainscot. There were noises outside, the wind playing through the forest leaves like sea breaking softly on shingle, the calls of night-birds, the croaking of bull-frogs. Life outside was going its own way, but inside, the house seemed holding its breath, waiting, listening, straining to hear something. Suddenly in some distant room upstairs, a swinging shutter clapped to, and a piercing cry like that of a lost soul rang through the house. She heard a stir where the children slept. They were awake now and their

fear seemed to seep through the lonely house. A door opened
and Mother O'Connor came to the head of the stairs, her face
white in the moonlight.

"What is it, Mother?" she whispered.

Julie Coutermarche was behind her.

"It's the ghost," she stammered. "They said this house was
haunted."

As they stood with their heads thrown back, listening to
catch the least sound, there came once more the noise of a body
falling, falling with a soft thump. Then the wail broke out
again, high pitched and unnatural. It died away in a hissing
noise, while the shutter flapped against the wall, and padded
movements aloft echoed down the well of the stairs. Then
pandemonium broke out. Shrieks, wails, and hissings filled the
air, rising high and fading away, pausing, renewing their
clamour while the floor shook with the bounding of bodies.
Julie Coutermarche clung to the banisters. Mother Duchesne
was laughing. She picked up a broomstick and began mounting the stairs.

"Bring a pail of water," she said to Mother O'Connor.

"Are you going to exorcise the ghosts?" asked Julie with
chattering teeth.

"Come and see," Mother Duchesne invited her.

As they neared the door of the garret room, screams and
cries became louder and wilder. Swiftly Mother Duchesne
turned the handle. From the beams that ran across the roof, six
wild eyes blazed down on them.

"Quick, Mother O'Connor," she cried, banging with her
broomstick against the wood. "Douse them well."

The water splashed up. With piercing cries, three wild cats
dropped to the floor, sprang window-wards and clawed their
way out over the sill and on to the branches of the tree below.

"I think we've laid the ghosts," Mother Duchesne laughed,
as she closed the wooden shutter over the open window, and
bolted it. Only the weird sounds of creatures out in the woods
could now disturb their night's slumbers.

There was plenty of cleaning to do the next day, though little enough furniture to arrange.

"I have put this house under St Joseph's care," said Mother Duchesne. "When Eleanor Gray becomes a novice in July and comes here so that we have a teacher for the boarders, she wants to take the name of Josephine. Our Lord's foster-father will look after us."

"Mother! Mother!" cried the children. "Look what's coming down the road!"

They all went out to see. A horse plodded along with a cart piled high with desks, tables, and benches. A globe was pivoting round on its axis with every jolt of the wheels. A pile of slates was stacked in a corner along with inkwells in a box. On the seat by the driver sat Fr Saulnier from St Louis, his face beaming. His feet rested on a large sack, and from time to time he glanced behind to where, at the end of a tethering rope, a fat cow ambled, protestingly lowing when the horse quickened his pace. The priest jumped down when they drew level with the door and came to Mother Duchesne with outstretched hands.

"Welcome! Welcome!" he said. "I knew you'd have nothing, so I've brought a few things along. There is all this school stuff from the boys' school that's closed down. It won't be needed until the Jesuits open their college. Wait a minute till I've unknotted this rope. Here, Mother O'Connor, you know how to look after cows. Whitefoot's quiet enough though she doesn't like walking far. Now this bag. Vegetables for you, Mother Duchesne. Potatoes, peas—any amount more where these come from—yours for the picking."

He came inside, noting what the nuns still lacked. He would let some of their former pupils know. Things would be forthcoming. There were arrangements to be made for the free school. That could start at once. And there were orphans waiting too. It was a pity the boarding school could not be begun till July as he knew some families who were waiting. He shook his head when Mother Duchesne suggested the children should go for the two months to Florissant.

R

"You'll never persuade the parents," he said. "They think it's a backwater. And so it is," he added to himself.

He approved of the proposed chapel. He and Fr Lutz would try to get out from time to time to say Mass for them. On 6 May he would celebrate in one of the upstairs rooms. Our Lord should bless the new house at the first opportunity. When he left, Mother Duchesne's heart was aglow with gratitude.

St Joseph showed his protection again. From Grand Coteau came a generous gift from Mother Audé. The bridge could be made, and the children's quarters improved. Friends in St Louis provided a ciborium. Mother Barat sent three more nuns from France, full of enthusiasm for the work.

They were surprised to find so much going on in so little space. An academy of twenty day children, an orphanage of nine, a free school of twenty-six, and a large Sunday school for negro women in quarters that were uncomfortably cramped. Mother du Tour, who had never felt the pinch of poverty in Missouri, wrote back to Paris. Mother Duchesne ought to build, ought to offer to American boarders something better than a basement dining-room and sugarless coffee in tin cups, ought to do things on a grander scale if she would have the same success as the houses in Louisiana. Mother Barat gave permission for a loan. Building could be begun.

Before the tabernacle in the basement chapel, Mother Duchesne accepted the new burden. The words of Fr de Andreis came back into her mind: "I am as sure that you will go among the Indians of the Osages as I am that you will go to bed to-night." Holy saints were not prophets. What a different future God was marking out for her! The loud singing of the crickets filled her ears and distracted her thoughts. She rose to remove a couple of slugs that were pulling their slimy lengths along the wall. This was a place most unworthy of her Lord. There must be a chapel built. They could have a dormitory above it. Perhaps it would not cost too much.

As she came upstairs, Mother Dutour, surrounded by a little group of children, called to her.

"Mother, do come and look at the curious things you can buy here. Louise, show Mother Duchesne your handkerchiefs."

The girl spread them out proudly, squares of calico printed all over. There was a complete calendar, the Signs of the Zodiac, and from the third the face of Napoleon Bonaparte looked out.

"Isn't it queer!" said Mother Dutour. "I wonder how important you have to be before people profit by selling your face."

"Thank God that will never happen to me," thought Mother Duchesne. There were compensations in being of no account. Yet the print eyes of the Emperor looked into her own, and seemed to speak to her of the futility of world conquest with a pathos that made the past suddenly near. This was the end of his ambitions. For her there could be no end until all the world was conquered for Christ.

The next years were not easy. The return to St Charles with Mother Mathevon was a golden interlude. Poverty, with the church of the Jesuits next door, was enviable. At St Louis, often they were without a chaplain. The priests of St Louis had many calls. The Jesuits who came to them from Florissant could never arrive before twelve. There could be no special feast days; Corpus Christi and the Feast of the Sacred Heart passed without Mass. Day after day in the week the nuns waited, fasting, for a priest who might or might not come. Then Fr van Quickenborne wrote to say that his priests could no longer serve them. Mother Duchesne's tears flowed bitterly. How could she bear the burden of Christ if He did not come to give her strength?

Thank God, He still left her some physical strength. In 1829, she journeyed to the southern houses again, convinced that the nuns in charge there were more worthy of preserving from discomfort and danger than herself.

"It is better to risk the health of an old creature like myself," she wrote to Mother Barat. She would not let her remain blind to her incapacity, her inability to accomplish any good. The Mother General was puzzled. She knew Philippine's humble opinion of herself, but there were others, too, writing to her from America, suggesting that she and her ways were old-fashioned. Was she in reality, or were they mistaking her adherence to the fundamental principles of the Society for out-of-date rigidity? Mother Barat prayed and waited.

Mother Octavie Berthold came in 1830 from Florissant to St Louis. Mother Duchesne knew her old companion was dying. Only a little while now and her loving heart would not be there to bring the comfort of old friendship. Octavie had a hard road of suffering to climb, but she would show the way gallantly to cowardly souls. Gratitude and grief filled Mother Duchesne's heart as she nursed her and watched hideous ulcers eat away the beauty that had once attracted all who met her. God was good to let her see how His graces transfigured a really holy soul.

It was strange to come from Octavie's bedside to the worldliness of some of the parents. It was as if their parties and outings and dancing and lukewarm Catholicism were the antics of marionettes. But that was her own fault. She had not learnt to win their hearts. That too was why so few children came to the Academy to learn to know the Heart of Jesus. Her fault. She would tell Mother Barat again how she spoilt everything.

In France Mother Barat began to believe her. There was the evidence of well-meaning people who wrote in the same strain. There was proof of success at Grand Coteau and St Michael's in the south where Mother Audé had been in charge. Philippine was old, undeniably. Lovingly, regretfully Mother Barat wrote to her.

"Far be it from me to blame you. I know only too well all that you have done and suffered. But times change, and we also must change and modify our methods. How many crosses, dear Philippine, Our Lord prepares for us. . ."

Perhaps Philippine would not think it a cross to be relieved of superiority. Mother Barat hoped the plan she had elaborated in her letter would not hurt too much. Two months later Mother Duchesne read it:

"My idea is to let Mother Thiéfry take your place in St Louis. . . You, dear Mother, may withdraw to Florissant or St Charles, wherever you may be most useful."

A wave of relief rushed over her. She would no longer spoil things, and yet God had not rejected her help entirely. Any position would be good where she could still go on serving Him. On 1 February 1832, she wrote back happily to Mother Barat, having told the good news to Bishop Rosati.

On 1 February he, too, wrote to France. The impending disaster must be prevented. His own great veneration for Mother Duchesne's holiness was based on true proofs of her religious spirit. He knew how many of the difficulties she faced were due to the imperfections of other people. He filled his letter with sober appreciation, begging the Mother General to reverse her decision.

"I believe there is no one among your religious who can gain as much confidence as Mother Duchesne justly receives here. All who know her respect and venerate her because of her virtues, which, joined to her age and the experience she has acquired during her long sojourn in this country, make her esteemed by all. . . No religious whom you may designate to fill the position . . . could really replace her. Let us follow, then, the guidance of Divine Providence; it will not fail to uphold us."

With what joy did Mother Barat read his letter! There was no delay in her reply to him, and the same day she sent another letter to her daughter.

"I yielded to His Lordship all the more readily since it cost me so much to make the former decision. . . I am delighted, my dear Philippine, to know that people are mistaken and that on your side it is humility alone that urged you to make that request. I trust that God will aid you, as He has done thus far, in the exercise of your difficult charge."

With a sigh, Mother Duchesne shouldered her burden once more.

Before the year was out, fresh trials were upon her. Cholera swept the Mississippi valley. There were deaths among the people of St Charles and Florissant, and the nuns there sickened. Mother Duchesne dispersed the school at St Louis, and prayed. Terrible as it was, cholera did not offend God.

"It is a scourge," she said, "but not a sin. Thank God the nuns have not died. They aren't fit for much at the moment, but they will get back their strength. We've so few labourers and the harvest is white."

Letters arrived from Mother Audé at St Michael's. With a stricken heart, Mother Duchesne read of the deaths of four of her community from the fatal plague, and of the illness of others. Weeks passed in anguish and uncertainty, until at length the news came that all were convalescent. Mother Duchesne turned to the building of a new wing at St Louis. Barns ready for the harvest—but who now would gather it in? A school must have its teachers. She had still to face the terrible death-agony of Mother Berthold. That was expected, but in the late summer Mother Audé sent her the shattering news that yellow fever had finished the work begun by the cholera and four more nuns were dead. Mother Duchesne began planning anew. The north must try to spare help for the south.

Broken and weak from her labours, Mother Audé sent a cry of distress across the sea to Mother Barat.

"Some time spent with you would strengthen me, would revive my poor soul and dispose me to suffer anew. Mother, dear Mother, will you allow me to come?"

Mother Barat sent for her. Mother Audé was to tell her about the American houses and then return with more assistance for them. Then the next year, perhaps the year after, it could be Philippine who could come back again to France. Surely America could spare her for a little while.

As the new building rose at St Louis, Mother Duchesne's thoughts turned to that other house, high and solitary, but more smiling above its river. Ste Marie, her first-born, had given so much glory to God. Perhaps this convent, too, her Benjamin, would be the means of spreading the love of the

Sacred Heart. There was, it seemed to her, something fitting in their resemblance. But she would never be able to love this one as she had loved Ste Marie.

A letter came from France. Gently Mother Barat told her that Ste Marie d'en Haut no longer belonged to them. Fortifications on the same hillside had ruined it for their work and it had been sold. A cry rose from Mother Duchesne's heart.

"I should sooner forget my right hand than that delightful place..."

But God willed it as He willed, too, that Eugénie Audé should serve the cause of America by remaining in France. Mother Duchesne carried on with the work at St Louis, serving all the servants of God. Though the number of girls in the academy was not high, the other schools were flourishing, and the children were spreading the effects of their training into the world. The stream of life was beginning to flow more smoothly in the early summer of 1834.

One morning on her way to the dormitories to call the nuns, Mother Duchesne stopped for a moment to watch the July sun play on the woods and grass slopes. God gave fair gifts. There was a beauty in all He did. In simple things lay sanity. She looked down at the new buildings nearing completion. There would be a grand school there, one day, fit for the new teaching that the changing world of industrial progress demanded. She thought, "I am quite out of fashion. Here you have to talk of science, astronomy, chemistry, philosophy. I feel all the more inclined to know Jesus only and no other science than that of the Cross. My patron saint for this year is St Andrew and his cross. *O bona Crux*!"

She went on to the bedrooms. As she made the rounds, none responded to her call. One and all had been struck down by cholerine.

Mother Duchesne acted swiftly. She isolated the sick, she dispersed the schools, she placed the orphans who were well in a separate building. Nurse and cook, she gave all her care to the invalids. With penance and prayer, she offered herself in expiation. Ruination faced her. The quarterly tuition fees of the thirty-two pupils of the academy, paid in advance, had to be refunded. The cost of living in a district that had been ravaged by illness rose alarmingly. Costs of building exceeded estimates. Alone with her orphans through the hot month of August, Mother Duchesne held the fort. In St Louis where cotton magnates and business men met to discuss the financial crisis, they would have smiled, pityingly or cynically, if they had seen in a quiet garden on the city's outskirts an old nun barefoot and with a rope knotted around her neck, following behind a procession of a dozen or so orphans who prayed, "*Parce, Domine, parce populum tuum, ne in aeternum irascaris nobis.*"

But the school at St Louis was still there in the autumn when many a once-flourishing warehouse had its shutters up. The superstructure had to be raised again, but the foundations had been firmly laid. Mother Duchesne began once more.

But in Europe Mother Audé's counsels prevailed, Mother Audé who had won American hearts and run American schools. Mother Barat thought of the weariness and labours that had been a foundress's lot and wrote to Philippine: "You need rest, and on that account an easier house to govern."

Quietly Mother Duchesne made her arrangements. Quickly the goodbyes were said. On 12 October she was back again at Florissant. The flaming maple trees greeted her. Separation was hard, but God was everywhere. She settled down again in the house she loved because it was little and lowly. As one year passed into another, there was much labour though few noted it. But in Paris Mother Barat knew, and planned and waited for the moment when life in Europe and America was more settled. It came at last and the letter was written and sealed. It was delightful to think of Philippine's joy when she opened it and read its loving message, "Come!" She knew her daughter's heart by reading her own. God had united them in understanding.

There were thousands of miles of Atlantic waves about the

American-bound ship when one of the passengers was pacing the deck. He did not notice, as he took out his pocket-book, that he let fall a letter entrusted to him for delivery by his wife who had been brought up by Mother Barat and liked to do commissions for her. The rectangle of paper slithered across the deck, was flicked up against a stanchion by a gust of wind, stayed poised there a moment, sank down again, then with a sudden quick movement slipped overboard.

As the months went by and Mother Duchesne made no movement to come to France, Mother Barat regretfully wrote again. Things in Europe now made her visit impossible. Only in heaven would they meet again. It was God's Will.

God's Will. The will of a Master Artist. Mother Duchesne put down the second letter, and put on her apron. There was gardening to do if her daughters were to be fed.

28: Eddies

MOTHER Duchesne was not certain what time the Mother coming specially from Paris to see them would arrive at Florissant. Reaching New York on 1 September 1840, Mother Galitzin planned to travel overland until the river steamer on the Ohio could be taken. A messenger from St Louis had said it was expected to berth that day and that a carriage would be ready for her. Everything in the convent had received its last polish, the convent man was posted as a lookout ready to say when the travellers were sighted, the few young religious were sitting with study books open and their thoughts on the Russian Princess whom they were to address now simply as Reverend Mother Galitzin, and the professed nuns were busy in boarding school and free school, hoping their charges would not appear at too great a disadvantage to one used to the children of the Hôtel Biron and the well-disciplined free scholars of France.

All was ready—all except the superior who, looking back on the years of her stewardship, wanted to cry out to one who came in the place of the Mother General, "I am an unprofitable servant!" If only the clatter of horses' hoofs along the road had meant that Mother Barat was moving nearer—if only the clap-to of a carriage door had meant that she was standing on Missouri soil, waiting, as she had waited thirty-six years ago, for her daughter to run forward and be taken to her heart.

With what joy would that daughter have kissed her feet! But
Mother Barat had written, "It is not in my power to go in person to that mission which has for so many years been the object
of my ardent desires. Evidently Our Lord has not judged me
worthy." Not worthy! If that was the judgement of the green
wood, what should the dry say?

It was a pitiful tale of inefficiency and failure that she would
have to tell. Florissant was the living witness to her power of
spoiling everything: a tiny boarding school, a free school for a
handful of children and the memory only of an Indian school
that had disappeared with the westward movement of the
tribes. Years ago she should have been removed from superiority. She had petitioned Mother Barat again and again, only to
be told that there was no one else to do her work. There was a
time after her illness of 1825 when she had hopes. Mother Audé
had come to see her and made her sleep on a bed, and Mother
Mathevon had urged Fr van Quickenborne to moderate her
penances. Quite rightly he had snubbed Mother Mathevon for
interfering; he knew her needs better. But then he had softened
in fear for her health, and Mother Mathevon had written such
an alarming letter to Paris that when it was a question of opening a new house, Mother Barat had thought of sending her
away from Florissant and its responsibilities. But Fr van Quickenborne had been alarmed then and had made out that she was
essential to Florissant, and so she had stayed on, and Mother
Audé had taken St Michael's foundation in hand.

Thank God, it had succeeded. Only sixty miles upstream
from New Orleans on the Mississippi, it promised well for the
future. Mary Ann Hardey had gone there, a very young head-
mistress but a perfect religious—Mary Ann Hardey who had
taken the name of Aloysia.

There was the foundation in St Louis in May 1827. It was
the twenty orphans that brought down blessings on that house.
It throve as soon as she could hand it over to a new superior
come from France.

But there had been joy when the Jesuits bought the Duquette

estate and summoned them back to their first convent at St
Charles. How well she remembered driving through the little
town with Mothers Berthold, Mathevon, and O'Connor, and
their whole worldly possessions of two mattresses, four quilts
and sheets, four glasses, six plates, a coffee pot, a frying pan, and
a stove. They were not going to starve, either, with twelve
pounds of rice, a pound of tea, a bottle of vinegar, a pillow-case
of brown sugar, and another of coffee.

The new bishop, Mgr Rosati, Fr Rector, some Jesuits and
three secular priests rode along with them and it seemed as if
the whole town was out, at doors and windows, to welcome
them with clapping hands and cries. The old log house was
locked and a villager climbed through a window to draw the
bolt. She smiled as she saw again the sight that met them—
there were no doors left to the rooms, no panes in the windows,
and holes gaped where the rotted boards had fallen away. Below, sheep and pigs had stabled for years, and the air was musty
and foul. There was dirt and decay everywhere. Mother
Mathevon had burst into merry song, as she dumped their belongings, set the carpenter to work on the broken floor, and
tucked up her habit for the fray. How happy they had been as
they cleared away the dirt and set a temporary altar where she
had placed the first one in 1818! At six in the evening they had
tinkled a little handbell and Bishop Rosati had filed in with
his twelve priests and they had sat on wooden benches while
they sang the office for the dedication of the church. God had
come back as He always did. When she had gone away, that
house had prospered, too.

The foundation at La Fourche had always been a thorn in
the flesh to her. Its spirit had never seemed quite in harmony
with that of the Society. There had been pain, too, when
Mother Barat had told her to summon all the American superiors to a meeting in 1829. She remembered how at St Michael's,
among all the young nuns brimful of ideas, she had felt like a
worn-out staff, good for nothing but to be thrown away, an
old lion without any strength to act, overwhelmed and anxious.

But for the sake of uniformity and to preserve the precious heritage they had brought from France, she had spoken and acted authoritatively, though none had fully realized that Mother Barat had meant her to act in her place. Perhaps they had represented afterwards to Mother Barat that she was old-fashioned and had pointed to the lack of success in the places where she worked.

They were quite right. She remembered when she had asked once more in 1831 to be put on one side and Mother Barat had yielded. What a pity that Bishop Rosati had put his foot down! He was quite wrong about her, but he had made Mother Barat keep her on as superior. Well, she could still thank God for everything—for the suppression of La Fourche, for the cholerine she had had to fight in school and community at St Louis, and for the gaps that cholera had made among the nuns at St Michael's. She could thank Him for Octavie Berthold who died in her arms in 1833, victorious after a bitter agony.

That was the year Mother Audé had gone from her. What a pang it had been to know that Eugénie would see Mother Barat and she herself would be thousands of miles away! God wanted it. She was far from all that had been the comfort of her younger days. Sister Manteau was at Grand Coteau, creeping round a few household tasks and praying. Sister Lamarre, still seeing the funny side of things, was fit for little more than long hours in the chapel at Florissant. Warm-hearted Mother Murphy had died. Amélie de Mauduit had died. She had felt like Jeremias lamenting over Jerusalem when Mother Barat wrote to her in 1833 to say Ste Marie d'en Haut was suppressed. That had been a bitter blow. "What happy moments we spent on that quiet solitary mountain of yours!" Mother Barat had said, and again, "Once we dwelt together on Mount Thabor. The vision was a brief one. Since then we have had to make Mount Calvary our dwelling place."

Looking back now, she had realized that the blow had been one of love. Nothing could take away the graces of those distant happy days. God had just detached her a little more, to make her fitter for His work here and now. Loneliness? Mother Barat had understood and had laid bare to her her own feeling of isolation, adding, "And yet it is a precious gift. God alone!" She thought again of the words she fancied she had heard nearly twenty years ago: "It is not by success, but by enduring contradictions that you are destined to please Me." Last year, even Florissant was on the verge of suppression. After three score years and ten, she had nothing to show. Yes, she would have to confess, "I am an unprofitable servant." Yet God had given her joys. She remembered how, two years ago, their negress had gone off with her little girl, thinking to better herself, and how, when the child was ill, she had crept back again. What happiness to make reparation in some measure! No one but herself had done the lowly offices of nurse for the piccaninny. The little black hands held hers trustfully, as she sat beside the cot and told of the loving Saviour who wanted His black child every whit as much as His white. Four of the boarding-school girls asked to accompany the Blessed Sacrament from the chapel to the bedside, and knelt while the dying child made her first and last Communion. They had carried the coffin to the cemetery, free-born Americans bearing the child of slaves. Perhaps some time in the future they would understand more fully the brotherhood of man.

There was a sudden noise of feet running up the path.

"Reverend Mother, she's here!" cried a sister.

The community gathered quickly at the door as the carriage drove up. A lively little woman stepped out, taking in with a quick glance all who were there to welcome her. From their midst, a tall, thin nun came forward and knelt to kiss her hand. As she rose, Mother Galitzin noted her bent shoulders, her face tired and lined, her faded blue eyes that were looking at her as simply as a child's. So this was Mother Duchesne. How old! When Mother Barat spoke of her, it always conjured up a picture of fire and energy. How shocked she would be to see now the reality!

Mother Galitzin was not one to waste time. She had been sent from France by Mother Barat to give every possible help to her American daughters. There would be things they required—things they had been going without. She had a quick eye to see where improvements could be of assistance to their work. As soon as might be, she asked Mother Duchesne to take her round Florissant.

"You need a lantern here to light these stairs," she said. She caught sight of wood from which the paint had peeled. "Get that repainted, dear Mother. Red would be a good colour. These locks are not very good. Who is your night visitor?"

"I do the locking up myself," said Mother Duchesne.

They moved through the little house and came to the infirmary. Gone were the times when Mother Duchesne had lain dying on the floor for want of money to buy beds, but it was still very poverty-stricken.

"You need more comforts for the sick," said Mother Galitzin. "Who looks after them?"

"I do," said Mother Duchesne. There was never anyone else who could be spared from the work of the schools. They could not teach either, after a night of watching by a sick bed.

"They say you help in the linen-room, too," said Mother Galitzin. Mother Duchesne would be killing herself with overwork. Aloud she said: "Don't you think the employments could be better arranged?"

Her eyes were travelling along the wainscot. "I should have those mouseholes stopped up," she added with a smile.

They went down together to the chapel. Mother Duchesne was thinking of the times when her Lord here in this tabernacle had been her only support. Mother Galitzin was examining everything.

"You'll need to make this a little more up to date," she said. "That old picture of St Francis Regis will never give devotion to the present generation. Take it down, and I will give you another of the Sacred Heart to take its place."

In silence Mother Duchesne watched Bishop Dubourg's

gift being lifted from its nail. Even her saint was leaving her. Should she tell Mother Galitzin that this picture replaced the one that had been burnt, the one that had watched over her since she found it among the rubbish at Ste Marie's and had vowed to honour it if St Francis sent her to the Indians? Better not. God spoke His Will through superiors.

Mother Galitzin was ready to see the garden.

"The beans are splendid this year," said Mother Duchesne. "They grew without any help from me. And the cabbages— look at the size of their leaves. It's such a blessing to have them for meals."

"They must be rather coarse that size," remarked Mother Galitzin with a smile. "I see you've had some peas and goose-berries."

Mother Duchesne sighed.

"No, the birds ate them all before we could stop them. It's only our big, sturdy apples that grow. One of the Jesuits' negroes pruned our trees. There weren't any strawberries. I have no success with the delicate plants."

Back in the house, Mother Galitzin thought over the situa-tion. She had been sent from France to help the American convents. She could do much by reorganization. Mother Barat had urged her to be charitable to all with the charity of the Heart of Jesus. Mother Duchesne was old, her labours had been long and hard. She was too old to be in charge still. A rest was what she needed. Some younger person was what her com-munity needed. She was too set in her ways to meet new things and adapt herself to them without pain. As she was, she was being a drag on the work. It was all very well for the com-munity to say she did all the work they were too busy or too ill to do. It was true that she did seem to have accumulated all the odd jobs of the house from the time she gave the call in the morning to the time she made the visit at night to see that all was safely locked up. But surely better organization could pre-vent that. This house was poor. Under a younger superior with different ways it might prosper more. Perhaps it was a mistake to keep Florissant going—a little piece of sentiment that was proving expensive, wearing out the valiant old nun. Mother Galitzin wondered if it might not be better in the long run to suppress the house. For the moment, however, her concern was with its superior. It would be better in every way to relieve Mother Duchesne of the burden. She would have to tell her as soon as possible.

There came a knock at the door. Mother Duchesne was there. Humbly, simply, she made avowal of her incapacity for good. It would be better if she were put on one side. Mother Galitzin jumped at the proposal.

"You need a rest, dear Mother," she said.

"I need time to pray and do penance for my sins," said Mother Duchesne.

"I shall send you to St Louis," Mother Galitzin went on. "Reverend Mother Grey is an old novice of yours. She will welcome you."

In October when the leaves were falling from the trees and their flaming colours turning to drab browns and greys, the few belongings of Mother Duchesne were put into the carriage and she drove away from Florissant. The flowery valley was misty—or was it that her eyes were dim so that she could not clearly see the house that had sheltered her hopes for so many years? God had given her so much more. She would try at last now to make Him some return. It was His kindness to send her to a place she was familiar with. She would ask Reverend Mother Grey for her old room. No one, surely, could need it. It was a little cupboard under the stairs. It would be quiet there and she would not need anything but a bed in it. And perhaps she would learn holiness at last through obedience. There would be time to spend in the chapel putting before God the labours of the Jesuits of Florissant among the Indians. She still had Fr Verhaegen's letter: "Pray that God may send labourers into this wild vineyard and that their works may be blessed to His greater glory." At seventy-one, prayer was still possible. It did not lie within her power now to plan a house among the

S

settlements to the west. Like Fr van Quickenborne, stout-hearted and self-forgetting, she must die and leave to younger workers the harvest of desires. Of what use now was the letter she had received in the summer from Bishop Rosati who had met Mother Barat in Paris and had learnt she was petitioning to help his Indians. "Go," he had written. "Follow your inspiration or rather, the Voice of God." God's voice had spoken and she knew her lot to be that of a simple religious, quietly doing the humdrum duties of each day.

Fr Peter de Smet knew exactly what he wanted. Since he had made peace in 1838 at Council Bluffs between the Sioux and the Potawatamies, there was no Indian who would not trust him. God's moment for conversions was at hand. But the apostle's work needed the support of holiness. Twenty years ago as a novice in the farm on the hill he had noted the holiness in the valley. He came eastward from the Upper Osage and sought out the Mother Visitatrix. She listened while he told of the Potawatamies of the Algonquins, hunters who had come southward into Indiana from Lake Huron and Lake Michigan in years gone by, a noble warrior race who honoured the Jesuit black robes of former days. She heard how they had been joined by a third band of Potawatamies whom the government had banished from their peaceful settlement not far from the towns of Liberty and Independence. Their holy Breton priest, Fr Petit, had gone with them through the November days when the soldiers had driven them forward with drawn bayonets away from the church they loved and the graves of their fathers. The Jesuits had received them as a precious legacy and Fr Petit had journeyed back to die in St Louis. He would plead his Indians' cause from heaven. His people needed a convent of the Sacred Heart, and nuns to teach the women and children, and Mother Duchesne to pray for them.

Mother Galitzin was cautious now. In Missouri, the convents did not seem to have answered to expectations.

"I can't see, Father," she said, "that any of them have accomplished much in the way of an apostolate."

"Believe me," he answered, "you'll never succeed in this country unless you call down the blessing of heaven by founding schools for Indians."

The Russian autocrat rose in her. She could not be overruled, though the apostle in her pleaded.

"That is our Mother General's greatest wish," she answered, and added with finality, "but we have neither money nor teachers."

"Nevertheless, Reverend Mother, it must be done," said Fr de Smet with equal finality.

As the sister let him out, he inquired after Mother Duchesne. The sister shook her head.

"Very feeble, Father, very feeble. She won't have the fresh air at St Louis that she was used to at Florissant. Perhaps when winter's past and spring is here, she'll get busy in the garden again."

"My garden," said Peter de Smet, "is the immense forest bordering the largest river in the world."

There was room in it for many gardeners.

On 6 January 1841, Mother Duchesne had been with the Magi offering gifts. She thought long about the myrrh. It was like the life-blood of a tree, shed drop by drop. It was mingled with the wine the women of Jerusalem offered to the Saviour on His way to Calvary. Nicodemus brought it to His burial, closing the gaping wounds. Myrrh had been brought to the Infant God because He was also Man. He was to suffer, and so to enter into His glory. She was roused from her meditations by a summons to the parlour. Fr de Smet wished to see her.

He rose as she entered and greeted her with the respectful affection of a son who knows how much his mother has done for him in the past. Characteristic things stood out in his memory: the precious sugar sent along from the convent when Fr Rector had wanted his young men to celebrate St Ignatius's Feast with due solemnity, the patch she had skilfully put on his cassock, the altar cloth sent to replace their rag, the banner of Our Lady painted and mounted with such care for the distant

tribes they were visiting. But behind all these was the steady
stream of her love and holiness. She had been there in the background, cradling their efforts. She was too humble to lay
claims to motherhood, but as she listened to him on this Feast
of the Epiphany, with the snow white on the old roofs of St
Louis and the footsteps of passers-by muffled in the streets, the
years slipped away and the call of the Redskins came clearly as
when she looked out on to the snowy roofs of Grenoble from
the lost heights of Ste Marie's. She had been so ill on Christmas
Day that she had prayed for release. Had God not answered her
prayer because He needed her still?

"You must write to Mother Galitzin," Peter de Smet said.
"You will get me the teachers she says she has not got, and I
will get you the money. It is our duty to conquer the Rocky
Mountains for Christ."

They smiled at each other.

"It is so sweet to serve God gratuitously and at our own expense," said Mother Duchesne as they parted.

Their petition followed Mother Galitzin down south to
Louisiana. Fr de Smet arrived with five hundred dollars he had
collected. Mother Duchesne wrote offering herself as a super-
numerary, "helping in the house and working, so as to supply
the place of some novice you would have sent".

The whole affair was fantastic, thought Mother Galitzin,
looking round with pleasure on the prosperous good works of
Louisiana. Prudence cried out against it, but Bishop Rosati had
come from Rome to Paris with a message to Mother Barat that
Gregory XVI had said how happy he would be to hear that the
nuns of the Sacred Heart were going to work among the
Indians, and the Holy Father's wish was law to the Mother
General. Mother Galitzin began to make arrangements.
Mother Mathevon should go. Twenty years ago, Mother
Barat had said to her, as she bade farewell to France, "I have
always had an ardent desire to go as a missionary among the
savages, to teach them the knowledge of God and so extend the
kingdom of Christ. My dear Lucille, I send you in my place."

Mother O'Connor should go. She had had experience in the short-lived Indian school at Florissant. Sister Amyot should go. As a Canadian, she had understanding of conditions. She wondered who else could be spared. Certainly not Mother Duchesne. That idea was preposterous. But she had not torn up a letter from Mother Barat and the words stood out without blur: "Remember that good Mother Duchesne in leaving for America had only this work in view. It was for the sake of the Indians that she felt inspired to establish the order in America. I believe it enters into the designs of God that we should profit, if possible, by the opportunity."

"Folly, but God takes the foolish things," Mother Galitzin decided against her better judgement. She took up her pen finally and wrote on 4 June: "Mother Duchesne according to the doctor is in constant danger of death, but she has insisted on fasting and abstaining during Lent... She feels at last she is dying and yet if a permission from our Venerable Mother arrives, she will take it as an order and no one will be able to stop her."

The permission arrived. Mother Duchesne made ready. Fr Verhaegen would conduct them there, leaving St Louis on 29 June. There was a further joy in store for her. Edmund, the negro servant, strong, capable, industrious, came to her with a broad smile on his black face.

"I'm coming with you, too, Mother," he said.

White, black, and red, all working together in God's vineyard—how good God was!

People talked and criticized. To take an old woman nearing seventy-three, sick and worn out with labour, was madness. What could she do?

Fr Verhaegen had been one of the novices at the farm on the hill. He knew Mother Duchesne as Fr de Smet knew her.

"Let her come," he said. "If she cannot work, she will forward the success of the undertaking by her prayers."

We wrestle not against flesh and blood, but against spiritual wickedness, against the rulers of darkness, he thought. The conquest of souls is first and foremost a spiritual thing.

29: Indian Summer

LITTLE Owl let his brown body slide noiselessly over the surface of the rock till he reached the edge. He lay in the shadow of the crag above, but the brown lichen beneath him was still warm from the noonday sun. The bright blue sky was empty. Far away below, the boy could hear the chirping of little birds and sudden jets of song from a mocking bird. There was no note of fear in their noise. Cautiously he peered over the lip of the rock, and only a tightening of his muscles betrayed his joy. There beneath him, a little to the right, lay the eyrie. Twigs and sprays of pine were woven together on the ledge backed by the rock face. He had been right, then. This was where the eagles nested. But he had found the way up to it too late in the year. By the second week in July, the eggs were hatched and the fledglings flown. Next year he would come again but earlier: not once but many times. But alone. He would learn to trail the great birds as silently as his father on the warpath.

Now there was no need to go warily. His eyes travelled over the scene below. The green forest trees moved like the waves of the Great Lakes, across the valley and up the distant hills. There were squirrels frisking in their branches, he knew, but he could not see them. He was so high up that even the wigwams in the clearing looked as tiny as birds' nests. There was smoke curling up in thin little wisps. One came from the log

cabin of Joseph Bertrand. Little Owl understood him, son of
French father and Indian mother, but he stood in awe of the
white wife he had brought back from Michigan. She would
have no Indian boys inside her cabin. Another smoke twist was
from the Black Robes' hut. Father Aelen was there alone now.
Fr Verhaegen and the mighty Fr de Smet had disappeared
through the woods to the lands where the palefaces lived. The
boy knew, too, where the other three French families had their
homes farther away in the woods, and he could see the log
cabin roofs of the two American settlers down by the creek,
where the country began to open out into prairie land. That
was where you could see the track that led in a few hours to the
camp of the soldiers. Fr Verhaegen said they were there to pro-
tect the Indians against white men who broke the law by in-
vading their territory. As for the tribes who were not Catholic,
if they attacked, it would be Potawatami tomahawks that
would be their safeguard. His hand slipped down to his belt
and fingered the sharp edge of his knife. He knew how to scalp,
though Fr de Smet preached about the peace pipe.

Little Owl's eyes wandered to the clearing near the village.
There was maize growing there. The Black Robes had shown
them how to plant it, but that was work for women. He was a
hunter. Fr Verhaegen had told him that the Great Spirit was a
hunter, too, tracking down the souls that fled from Him as
swiftly as the deer when they had winded Little Owl. The
Great Spirit dwelt with His Potawatami children down there
in the log church. He had made Himself a white man and had
let Himself be tortured and put to death by the palefaces for
love of His Indian tribes. That was why the Black Robes came
to them and why the women of the Great Spirit were coming,
too. He wondered what they would be like. He remembered
the statue of Mary, Mother of the Great Spirit, with her long
robes and flowing veil, and decided they must resemble her.

The rock beneath him was growing cold. He moved back
from the edge, slithering from boulder to boulder till he
reached the wood. Through the maple trees the shafts of sun-

light played on the stream that gurgled down the hillside. The
white scut of a rabbit caught his eye. Little Owl fitted his arrow
and let fly. He ran forward and seized his booty. As he passed
the Black Robes' cabin, he laid it at their door. There was an
emptiness about his middle that made him seek out his own
wigwam. His little sister looked up as he lifted the flap, but he
waved her away while he helped himself to the corn mush that
hung in its pot over the fire. But when she placed some raw
dog's flesh in his wooden bowl, he thawed towards her, and
listened while she told him the news. The two warriors that the
tribe had sent out had found Fr Verhaegen and the women of
the Great Spirit at a farm eighteen miles away by the Osage
river. They had knelt before the Black Robe and asked his blessing; then the women of the Great Spirit had made them sit
while they themselves fed them. The two had eaten what was
set before them though it tasted strange, for they had feared to
offend by refusing it. Then the Black Robe had promised they
would be at Sugar Creek the next day, and they had mounted
their horses again and made their way back to announce the
glad tidings.

"We are all going out to meet them," she said proudly at
the end.

"I shall need my best blanket," said Little Owl. He was not
old enough to ride out with the warriors, but he could wear an
eagle's feather in his black hair. It was a great event. The whole
tribe would be out in gala array. That night Little Owl could
scarcely sleep for excited anticipation.

Eighteen miles away, Mother Duchesne watched through
the window of a log cabin and saw the sky turn dark and great
stars come out. The moon rose and silvered the clouds that
drifted by. There was a trickling stream somewhere near and a
soft rustling of trees all around. An owl cried out. In the distance another answered. A sharp bark spoke of a fox on the
prowl. The summer night for all its slumberous warmth
seemed full of life and movement. Mother Mathevon and
Mother O'Connor were fast asleep; Sister Amyot too. When

you were young, sleep came more easily. Her mind was too full
of the scenes of the last week for her to rest. How good God
was! On the river steamer that took them up the Missouri, He
seemed to have given her back her life, and spread before her
an entrancing, ever-changing picture of majestic bluffs, and
wooded islands and steep grassy slopes that bordered the ash-
coloured river, as though He smiled upon her journey. He had
shown her, too, towns and villages that had no churches, and
people had come on board when they stopped and besought
them to stay. She must pray that more labourers should come
into His harvest. The fields were growing white. On 4 July
Fr Verhaegen had preached to the passengers and they had
clapped and stamped their feet with approbation when he had
finished. There was a real spirit of brotherhood among them.
As of old, it sought to express itself in the symbol of a shared
meal. That was why she had accepted with the rest the iced
sherry that celebrated Independence Day and the freedom of
man in his essential rights. It was like a message from her father
as, after all these years, she neared her goal. The passengers had
been so generous, too. They had taken up a collection for the
Indian mission and there were dollars and provisions for winter
to enrich them. At Westport there was a crowd of Indians in
the streets about the landing stage, and as Fr Verhaegen pointed
out their different costumes, it seemed to her as if representatives of all the Six Nations must have gathered before her. Four
days on the river, and twice four days in a jolting ox-wagon,
and here she was almost at her journey's end. As the sky through
the window flushed and brightened to blue, her heart was too
full for words. What were the years gone by, in the eternal eyes
of God? The child listening in the house of the Place St André,
the novice reading of Xavier, and the nun seeing the Magi's star
in the convent on the hill above the Isère, the secretary on her
knees before Mother Barat in the Rue des Postes, the traveller
from the *Rebecca* kissing the muddy soil of Louisiana, they
were all one, all here, waiting, waiting—and the final summons
had come.

"Mother," said Lucille Mathevon, knowing what this day meant, "the ox-wagon is ready. The sooner we start, the better."

They were silent as they jolted and swayed on the forest track, while the dew was on the grass and the birds called in the trees.

Little Owl was up betimes, too. He watched in silence while his father tied his black hair on the top of his head, letting it hang down his back in a long tail. Then the strong arms, blue with their twisting tattooings, took red paint and marked great circles round his eyes. On his head he set lofty plumes, on his feet his moccasins with their bright-coloured porcupine quills, round his waist he fastened a belt of wampun, and hung a gorgeous blanket about his shoulders. Little Owl's eyes half closed with delight as his father stepped out into the early morning sunshine, vaulted on to his horse, and cantered away along the trail. He turned his attention to his big sister. She had put on her gala blouse of crimson fastened at the neck with a deer's foot. Below her blue petticoat, her gaiters showed their sky-blue embroidery and porcupine quills, and beaded moccasins were on her feet. She had vermilioned her face, and put a band of blue beads round her black hair. It only needed the blue blanket now and the skunk perfume to make her fit to take her place among the women of the tribe. They were already gathering outside on the open prairie. Fr Aelen, nervous as a wild cat for her kittens, walked among them and placed benches outside the mission house door. What would the nuns think of his children?

"What splendid men!" cried Mother Mathevon as two horsemen appeared suddenly at the top of a rise and bore down upon the wagon at full speed. Reining in, they brought their mounts to an abrupt halt, and saluted the Black Robe and his companions.

"They've come to show us the safest and best road," Fr Verhaegen explained, as curveting and wheeling, the horsemen took the lead.

The chief, magnificent in feathered headdress, advanced. . .

Two miles further, two more horsemen galloped down on them, and still another pair. By the time they were near the village, there was a great band around them, spreading out on the prairie in circles and semi-circles, charging in again, each horse stopping dead close to the wagon. Mother Duchesne's eyes gleamed. These were warriors after her own heart. What warriors of the Lord they would make!

"I'm afraid you'll have to go through all the ceremony," Fr Verhaegen whispered to Mother Mathevon as Fr Aelen helped them to alight and took them to the benches.

The chief, magnificent in feathered headdress, advanced and spoke, while Joseph the half-breed interpreted.

"What happiness for us to see in our midst the women who have sacrificed all to come here to instruct our children in the true religion," he began.

What happiness! Mother Duchesne forgot the rest of the speech. What happiness! A reality; no longer a dream. Redskins all about her, simple, loving, eager for the Faith.

Mother Mathevon whispered, "His wife says they are all going to shake our hands to show their joy at our arrival."

The men and women were all lined up. One by one they came forward, seven hundred of them, and shook the nuns by the hand. It was a pity, thought Little Owl as he watched his big sister make the sign of the cross as she approached the women of the Great Spirit, it was a pity he was not a little older so that he could get more close to the Good Old Lady who, Fr Verhaegen had just said, had been waiting thirty-five years to come to them.

After the reception, the Jesuits took them to the church. The simple log hut was large enough to hold some hundreds of Indians. Near by were the graves of those who had died in the Faith.

"There have been holy souls among them," said Fr Aelen. "I have sometimes found at Holy Communion that the Sacred Host has left my hand and placed Itself on the tongue of a poor Indian."

The woman from Michigan came forward.

"You'll be dead tired," she said. "You must come to my home and have a meal. I know what it's like when they begin palavering."

Fr Verhaegen came to them full of apologies. They had not been notified in the village when the nuns would come. No preparations had been made for their house, but Manope, a good Catholic, had offered his cabin. He had moved out, family and all, and taken up his quarters in an unused covered wagon. Mother Mathevon accepted his offer for her little community.

Edmund met her, a broad grin across his black face.

"I put in your baggage, Mother. The trunks and provisions are all there. I found two chairs for you. I found some boards to make a bed for Mother Duchesne. The kitchen is in the open air. There's no more room inside. I measured the cabin. Fifteen feet by twelve. Never mind. Fr Aelen says he will get each brave to cut a log, and then I will show them how to build a proper convent for you."

Edmund was basking in unwonted admiration. All the time the nuns were within, he had been followed round by a silent string of Indian boys. He had known he was creating an impression as he undid his tool chest, and knocked up the bed for the cabin. He, Edmund, could teach these savages.

The nuns were restless that first night, tossing and turning in their blankets on the earthen floor.

"Manope didn't take all his belongings," thought Mother Mathevon. "I must be attacked by a variety of every known carnivorous pest. Why do holy authors write so much about the savage customs of the heathen tribes and omit to say anything of the more savage onslaughts of the insect ones?"

It was hard to keep the place clean. Each day brought them so many visitors. Little Owl entered with his father and sat down in silence on the floor to watch. There was bedding, the like of which he had never before seen. There were books. There were needles and thread that the nuns used with a skill that far surpassed that of the Potawatami women. His father would send his little sister to the school that had opened in the shed the black man had made for them. She would learn how to make him the clothes he needed. His big sister would come to the nuns, too. He and his father were watching through the open door the Sister Nun at work with pots and frying-pan over the fire outside. It would be well if she taught their women folk to prepare food that smelt so savoury. He watched the Good Old Lady. She could sit as still as any Indian, while she peeled vegetables or sewed or let the beads of her rosary slip through her fingers. The Reverend Mother and the Catechism Mother could already begin to talk to them in their own tongue. The Good Old Lady talked to him with her smile and her eyes. At the end of three hours, his father rose and he filed out after him in silence. Little Owl knew where the red hen had made her nest. He went off on his own errand. The next morning he placed an egg before the cabin door.

"For the Good Old Lady," he said to Mother Mathevon as he slipped away.

"Here's a birthday present for you to celebrate your seventy-third anniversary," said Mother Mathevon. It took some persuasion to make Mother Duchesne accept these extras. "We'll need to have a day of happy thanksgiving. It's only just over a month since we started the school, and there are forty-two children in it."

"When they are in it," laughed Mother O'Connor. "Fr Verhaegen had to go all through the woods on horseback yesterday to round them up."

"Then look at the presents we get—cucumbers, corn, rabbits, prairie chicken—we shan't be short of food, what with the cow Fr Aelen has given us, and the vegetables from his garden."

Sister Amyot said, "But we'll need to keep our eyes on the prairie dogs if we're not to starve. I don't know how they get in—through the chinks, I suppose, or by burrowing up through the floor. Only yesterday, I put a side of bacon down

Little Owl watched the Good Old Lady.

on a wooden box while I turned to get the frying pan, and before you could say knife, one of the little beasts had snapped it up and was off."

"I'm going to bring the little girls along to sing for you," said Mother Mathevon. "They've lovely voices and they've picked up the tunes beautifully. They know Fr Barat's hymn to the Sacred Heart, though they're singing their own words."

As she listened, Mother Duchesne did not know whether the tears in her eyes were those of sorrow or joy. What would she not have given if the composer had been beside her to share in her fulfilled desires! He was old and ill. Yet his youthful ardour was here with her as the songs that had echoed among the grey stones of Ste Marie's rang out among the maples of Sugar Creek. Perhaps old age did not matter if the spirit lived. When she saw what Christianity had done for the Potawatamies, her heart went out to the unconverted Indians. "If Alexander the Great wept on the shores of the ocean because he could not carry his conquests further, I might weep also at the thought that my advanced age prevents me from saving so many poor people," she reflected. The longing must be entrusted to the Sacred Heart.

The log convent on the hill by the church was rising section by section, under Edmund's skilful supervision. By October the single large room which was to serve them for everything was ready. The cracks of the walls were stuffed with mud, and heavy cotton cloth was stretched over the walls and ceilings. Before a silent, awe-stricken audience, Edmund whitewashed it. The bedding was carried up, the two chairs, the table he had made them, and the cooking pots and pans duly arranged in the corner they had named the kitchen. Fr Verhaegen came upon Mother Mathevon down on her knees, coaxing the fresh fire to burn in the new hearth. She looked up with a laugh as he stood watching the little community.

"You really are Potawatamies now," he said. "They were once members of the Ojibways and Ottawas, but they went out from their midst and made a new hearth fire in a new land.

That is what their name means—Potawatamies, the Fire makers."

"So we have gone out from our land and made a new hearth fire," Mother Mathevon reflected. She was thinking of the land of Dauphiné. "The tribe carries its fire with it, doesn't it, Father?"

"And the others are lit from the one that is brought," said Fr Verhaegen. In the background, Mother Duchesne was knitting. He nodded in her direction. "There's your fire—a burning and a shining light."

"Kindled by the flames of Our Lord's Sacred Heart," said Mother Mathevon softly, "the only true Fire-Maker."

The winter was a desperately cold one. The cotton cloths bellied and flapped like the sails of the *Rebecca*, when the icy winds blew across the prairies. The snow was thick and the way to the church unmade. In the dark of the early mornings, they floundered into drifts, and got soaked to the skin. Within the church, it was below freezing point and the melted snow in their clothes turned to ice. The men of the tribe had gone off on their winter hunt. The blizzards often kept the Indian girls in their wigwams. Mother Mathevon laughed and sang, and Edmund, with his cheerful grin, went on with his building. By the time Mother Galitzin unexpectedly came to see them at the end of March, he had added a top storey.

"You have to go up this ladder," said Mother Mathevon, dexterously mounting the perpendicular steps, and lending a hand to the Mother Visitatrix. "Mind your head. You won't be able to stand up without knocking against the roof. Those boards are all right if you plant your feet fair and square on them—otherwise, they tip a bit and your leg goes through to the room below."

It was all very primitive, Mother Galitzin decided, but she was impressed with the Indians' devotion and fervour as she watched them approach the Holy Table on Palm Sunday. Surely their love would make up to Christ's Sacred Heart for the coldness and indifference of so many Christians. Through-

T

out the two days of her stay, there was a constant stream of visitors to greet her. There was a great work to be done here. When Mother Mathevon spoke of boarders from the distant Osage territory, she gave her consent. Only Mother Duchesne stretched on her plank bed worried her.

"I shall get out when the weather is better," said Mother Duchesne. "They are all so good to me here. I try to help a little."

She picked up a stocking from a large pile.

"They leave three hundred pairs at our door to wash and mend each week," she told Mother Galitzin. "I can sit with the dying, too. There is much illness at the moment. Even I am better than nothing."

Mother Galitzin shook her head, and went back east.

Spring came in all its fresh beauty of running water and bursting buds. The sap rose in the maple trees and the tribe went out to tap them for their sugar.

Little Owl climbed the boulders one day and cautiously peered over. The eyrie had fresh green sprays built into its last year's twigs. In the midst lay two eggs, one white, one speckled with rust coloured spots. There was a great rush of wings as the mother returned to the nest. Frozen against the rock, he watched her settle herself on the eggs. Then like a snake, he glided away.

Mother Duchesne watched Mother Mathevon do all she herself longed to do. She saw her run the errands for all who knocked at their door asking for help; she nursed the sick and washed their sores, she bathed the children who came as boarders, and cleansed their verminous clothes. She spoke to them in their own language, and set them singing. She never seemed to tire, and always her bright smile cheered people. Mother Duchesne found that though the birds were building and flowers were appearing and the forest was a tender green again, her old bones did not share that youthful resurrection.

"I do nothing," she told herself. But God did not need her in order to let fall His graces. Fr Aelen had told her of an Indian who had learnt of the Passion from his guardian angel as he walked in the woods. She often made her way to the little cemetery. It had a pretty fence and a gate, now, that Edmund had shown the Indians how to make. There was brotherly charity. She would say a prayer for all within, though some, the Jesuits said, were saints. "May my bones be happy enough to rest among theirs," she petitioned.

Little Owl was delighted when he found the eaglets hatched. Uncouth little creatures, they sheltered beneath their mother's wings. As the days went by, he saw their feathers grow and noted how they clamoured for food and greedily seized it from their mother's beak. It was amusing to watch their self-importance, when the sun struck bright on the eyrie; and to see them crouch cowering beneath the brooding eagle when a sudden spring shower drenched down from a grey sky. Then one day as he drew near the place, he found one of the eaglets lying dead at the foot of the rock. He picked it up, thinking, "It must have fallen. What a shame! It would have been a strong bird, and a beautiful one."

He found his observation post and looked anxiously over. The second eaglet was still there. Every day now seemed to make him finer and stronger. He was beginning to grow wing feathers. Up aloft his mother was a speck in the blue vault. Eagles could travel a long way.

Fr de Smet came and spoke to the nuns of his work in the Rockies. Spring was warming into summer. Mother Duchesne found she could walk more easily to the church and spend longer hours at prayer. She could knit and mend again, too. She wrote to Mother Barat, "I feel when I hear of the Rocky Mountains or other missions of that sort, the same longing desires I had in France to come to America, and in America, to be sent to the savages. They tell me people live to a hundred in the Rocky Mountains. Now that I am quite well again, and being after all only seventy-three, why should I not have ten more years of work before me?"

In the early days of June, Bishop Kenrick, the coadjutor bishop of St Louis, came to Sugar Creek. He was delighted

T*

with all he saw. With the brilliant sunshine on everything and
the Indians moving quietly about the village or seated in the
warm shade, he had stepped into an idyllic world. But the
warm-hearted woman from Michigan laid her mind bare to
him.

"It's a shame, My Lord, the way those nuns are living.
They'll kill themselves with kindnesses done to the lazy crowd
in the village. I grant you they're making a difference. The
women are getting quite civilized, and as for the girls, you'd
not recognize them. But they're savages still under their red
skins and it breaks out from time to time. Sister Amyot got the
fright of her life last week. They've a habit of leaving presents
at the door. You can guess what she felt like when she found a
row of scalps hung there. Then one of the girls got into the
cabin by herself and made a regular feast on all the raw meat
in the larder. Of course she was ill at night and it was Mother
Duchesne that suffered. They use those nuns' kindness as if it
was the water in the creek—they're sure to find it always there,
and cool and fresh. But I doubt whether they'll find the old
saint there when the winter comes again. All she can do now is
pray."

Bishop Kenrick used his eyes. On his return to St Louis, he
wrote to Mother Barat.

As June flamed towards July, Mother Duchesne's happiness
ripened. Could her old age have been better planned, among
her Redskins, with Lucille as her superior? It was so sweet to
talk with her of those early, happy days at Ste Marie's when they
were first getting to know Mother Barat and learning from her
to submit their apostolic longings to the greater love of Christ's
Sacred Heart. It was sweet to kneel in the church and hear the
rustle of the forest leaves and to pray for all the souls that lived
among the woods that stretched onwards to the Rocky Mountains. She was not fit for much, but God gave her long hours of
prayer.

Little Owl, off to his hunting, called in at the church. As he
thought, she was there, the Good Old Lady. She was there in

the morning, and there in the evening, as still before the Tabernacle as he was by the eyrie. No wonder the tribe had now found her name. She was the Woman who prays always. It seemed to Little Owl that she could not stop talking to God. She was praying if he met her under the trees or walking on the prairie. He had come across her once singing a little song in an old, worn voice. It was not like the clear notes of the Chief Mother or the mellow tones of Edmund, but he had recognized it as the hymn they sang to the Sacred Heart. Little Owl stepped quietly up the aisle and, kneeling behind her, lifted the hem of her worn habit to his lips. Then he crept out again and made his way to the woods.

He was in luck. The eaglet was moving from side to side of the broad nest, flapping his wings to exercise them. In a few days' time, perhaps, he would be ready to fly. The mother sat on a ledge above and watched him. Then she swooped down and returned with a rabbit in her talons. He was not yet old enough to feed himself, and he moved towards her trustfully expectant.

There was little to do in the village throughout the hot summer days. The men sat immobile, their heads on their knees. Little Owl's little sister had still to go to the nuns' school, sitting under the trees, sewing and singing and saying the catechism. He was free to watch the eyrie, spending the long hours silent and still in the shadow of the cliff. Any day now the eaglet might take flight. He would move across to the edge of the nest, beating his wings. He would sit with steady eye on the sun and watch his mother drop down out of the blue. But as yet his courage failed him. Little Owl watched him cringe back each time from the abyss, and take shelter in the nest. Why should he take the plunge? The mother bird was there to bring him food. But the morning came when she was not there. Desperately he called for her and she did not answer. There was no food left in the eyrie. Evening came and he was still alone. So was it the next day, and the next. At midday, Little Owl saw the eaglet look pitifully round the nest. The twigs and sprays were flat and

comfortless, there was no one there to shelter him with her
wings or give him the food he cried out for. He moved to the
edge and seemed to look down to the treetops far below. The
summer breeze ruffled his plumage. Suddenly the great span
of his wings was outstretched and he launched himself into the
void. For a moment he sank down, then he swept round and
righted himself. He was caught in a rising stream of air and
Little Owl saw him moving up and up towards the sun as he
disappeared behind the cliff.

The boy relaxed. That watch was over. The eagle would
never return to the eyrie. That had played its part and was done
with. He let his glance roam again over the scene below, where
in the midst of the trees thin wisps of smoke rose up. One now
came from the cabin of the nuns, which looked, at this distance,
tiny as the eyrie beneath him. He suddenly fixed his gaze on an
ox-wagon that was moving away from it, down the track that
led to the prairie and the Osage river. He could see two people
in it. One was Fr Verhaegen, the other the Woman who prays
always. Why were they going?

As they jolted and swayed on the road that went eastward
to Westpoint and the Missouri steamer, Mother Duchesne
offered her pain for the souls of Redskins.

"God knows the reason for this recall, and that is enough,"
she thought. Truly now she had nothing left to cling to. It was
God alone.

30: Portage

A FEW days later a boat was steaming down the Missouri and into the Mississippi. When it berthed, Mother Duchesne stepped on to the landing-stage at St Louis. It was the last time she would journey on the Father of Waters. Things had changed since she had first seen its turgid waters close on a quarter of a century ago. But the graces the river had brought her had flowed and still flowed as ceaselessly as its own full stream. It had brought her graces of sorrows and graces of joys. Like all men, she had not gratefully corresponded with them. But she would have some years still left to do penance, for herself and for all men. This New World to which she had given herself held so many great possibilities, marred, like herself, with so much that was evil. The love of the Heart of Jesus alone could make plain its problems. As the carriage bore her away from the Mississippi, over the hills to St Charles, she was resolving afresh, "I will live a penitent and mortified life."

The convent she returned to was not the old familiar log building that had seen their first trials and heartenings. That had gone with the old familiar faces, and a newer and finer brick structure had taken its place.

They gave her a little room not far from the chapel. It had only a small bed, a chair whose seat was of raw hide, a couple of holy pictures, her few devotional books and a box containing her greatest treasures—the letters that Mother Barat had written to this dearest of her daughters. They gave her a little work to do in the parish school. Each day she made her way, with her slow, painful step, to the semi-basement rooms opposite the kitchen where the French-speaking children learnt from her to sew, and read, and say their catechism and to love God. In the warm autumn days when the fruit was ripe, she went out with the community to pick the rosy apples to send to Sugar Creek for tarts. They were a treat for the Indian children.

"I can't put away the thought of the Indians," she said, "and in my ambition I fly to the Rockies. I can only adore the designs of God in depriving me of the object of my desires."

There were many things He was depriving her of in His merciful plans.

In 1846, Florissant was suppressed. He had permitted her prayers to save St Charles, the first of all her houses, but Florissant, still dearer to her for the labours and anguish it had caused her, for the memories of her first companions, of Bishop Dubourg and Fr de Andreis and Fr van Quickenborne, for the countless graces she had received, for the coming of the first Indian children, Florissant was taken from her. She offered to live there with one sister if only it could be saved for the sake of the day school and the care of the church.

"If I am refused," she wrote, "I shall submit but I shall never be consoled."

The blow had to fall.

"Ste Marie and Florissant are like two swords in my heart," she said. "I shall feel them till my last breath."

Sister Manteau had died at Grand Coteau in 1841. The next year it was Mother Audé who died in Rome. Bishop Rosati died before he could return from Europe to his diocese. At Florissant in 1844 Sister Lamarre's cheerful soul went to her Maker while the organ played the music she had asked for. News came from France in 1845 that Fr Louis Barat had died. The loneliness of old age was about her, as one by one the companions of her strong youth grew wrinkled and white-haired

and fell asleep in death. But Mother Barat still lived, Mother
Barat who had won her heart so completely from the first
moment of their meeting on that December day at Ste Marie's,
Mother Barat who understood her heart so completely. She
warmed each time with fresh life when the post arrived from
France.

But one day in 1845 the post came, and it brought no letter
to her from Mother Barat. Disappointed, she yet accepted the
disappointment. She could not expect to hear from her with
every courier. But the next post came, and still there was no
letter for her.

Mother Duchesne wrote back, making no mention of her
pain. The business of the Society must be overwhelming, she
told herself. Duty must come before friendship. But as the
year wore on, it was hard to bear the absence of a letter for herself when others were happily reading notes from the Mother
General. Should she go on writing herself? It was a relief to
know that Mother Barat listened to her, even if she gave no
reply. But perhaps this was just another stronghold of selfish-
ness in herself. Perhaps the silence meant a rebuke. After all,
who was she that she should take up the precious time of the
Mother General, were it only by making her read?

"It shows me," she wrote, "that I must keep myself more
aloof."

It grieved her heart, but thereafter Mother Duchesne herself stopped writing. It was the hardest sacrifice left for her to
make. God knew now that she wanted to make reparation at
no matter what cost to herself. "I must have committed some
fault," she thought, "and my dearest Mother has lost all affection for me. It feels as if my heart was withered with grief."

In Paris as the ships from America brought no letters
from Mother Duchesne, Mother Barat grew more and more
alarmed. What had happened to Philippine that for nearly two
years she answered none of her letters, that she gave no reply to
her anxious inquiries? The Mother General grieved at the
thought that old age had perhaps estranged her loving mind.

With the years, she longed more and more for the companionship of the one person whose burning love and fiery zeal had best understood her own, and now that dearest friend kept silence. Mother Amélie Jouve, who had so well taken the place of her sister Aloysia, was leaving France in 1847 to be a superior in Canada. Mother Barat called her to her.

"Missouri is a far cry from Canada," she said, "but you must visit St Charles before you go to your own house. You must see your dear aunt, and tell me everything you can about her. Here is a letter for her, and presents. You must give her news of all your family and of all her old friends here in France. You must ask her from me if there is anything at all she would like, anything at all that we could give her. My dear Amélie, you go in my place. Do whatever you can for her. And let me know as soon as you can if there is anything wrong."

On the spot, as representative of the Mother General, Mother Amélie Jouve discovered the trouble.

"The letters Mother Barat wrote have never arrived—her messengers have been careless or unfortunate—there are so many miles of land and sea between Paris and Missouri!" she thought. "I could rail against fortune but I know what my aunt and what Mother Barat would say. God permitted it. Those two holy saints of God have accepted the pain—well, they are the holier for it. But now, what joy it will be to both of them to know that neither on the one side nor the other had love cooled."

It was an ecstasy of joy that transfigured Mother Duchesne's face as she received Mother Barat's letter from her niece.

"I might be an angel from heaven," thought Amélie Jouve, "whereas she certainly is a great saint. I shall write to Mother Barat and say, like St Anthony, 'I have seen Paul in the desert.'"

She had to bend forward to catch her aunt's words, so weak had her voice become.

"What, our Mother General still thinks of me, still cares for me?" Mother Duchesne said. "She has been so good as to send you to me?"

"She wants to know if there is anything you would like," her niece went on. Mother Duchesne looked puzzled.

"But I have everything now," she said. "Do you see how near to the chapel my room is? How can we complain when we have Jesus in the tabernacle?"

Mother Jouve insisted.

"But it's our Mother's wish that you should ask for something."

There was a long pause while, beneath the half-closed lids, the old eyes looked back into the past.

"There was a picture of St Francis Regis that was a gift of Bishop Dubourg," she said at last. "It was once in the chapel of Florissant. Then it was taken down—but before Florissant was suppressed. If it could be found, I would like to honour it again."

"Yes," said Mother Jouve. "But that is not enough. What more would give you joy?"

Again there was a pause. Memories of the hard and happy days of Florissant thronged into her mind. Death had reaped so many that were dear to her, even among her first daughters. But Mother Hamilton was still alive, one of her very first choir novices, one who had fulfilled all her hopes of what America could give. She was a superior now.

"It would be wonderful to be the daughter of Mother Hamilton," she said aloud. "I would love to end my days in her care."

Mother Jouve wrote to the Mother General, and made known her aunt's wishes. Too soon the time for parting came. She watched with thankfulness the way in which the younger nuns treated the holy veteran.

"They venerate her as a relic," she thought, with the insight of a Duchesne, "but to my way of thinking it makes her sad to be only a relic." There was a last message from her aunt to her.

"Our Lord has called us to follow Him carrying the cross as He did. . . See God always in His creatures and live with them as children of one Father."

White, red, black, children of one Father, they were all in
Mother Duchesne's prayers, and all could profit from her
sufferings.

It seemed at one time that God was going to ask for the
sacrifice of her mind. They had taken from her all work in the
school except the teaching of catechism to a tiny group of
French-speaking day children. She found herself forgetting
things, and her eyesight became weak so that she could not
do even the coarse sewing that for some time past had con-
tented her once skilful fingers. She accepted God's Will, and
offered this last gift with both hands.

"You have to be quite convinced that God ordains everything for our greatest good," she said, "and then you can face
boldly the humiliating state in which loss of reason places you."

But God only wanted her consent. Her mind remained
strong, though her body year by year lost its vigour. He sent
her joys.

Fr de Smet wrote to her of his work in the Rockies. He had
baptized twelve hundred Indians and still there was work to
do. He asked her to pray for them, speaking of their debt of
gratitude to her.

"After fulfilling the Will of God here below, and when you
are receiving the reward of your labours in heaven, you will
pray very specially for our poor Indians," he wrote.

Of course she would, and did. But he was wrong in thank-
ing her. It was Mother Mathevon who worked for the Indians.
How she had thrilled when they told her of the heartbreaking
driving away of the Potawatamies from Sugar Creek in 1847;
in despair at seeing their fertile fields, the labours of their hands,
taken from them by the white men, the warriors had sullenly
rebelled at the thought of having to begin again in their fresh
territory, and it had been Mother Lucille who had gallantly
crossed the river and shown them how to cut the tall prairie
grass in their new home. The mission had life still.

Fr Verhaegen called on her whenever he could and told her
stories of his work among the Indians. They had power to

make her old heart beat with admiring zeal. The Jesuits had reached the strongholds of the mountains, now, and he spoke of the great silent snow peaks, so like the mountains of Dauphiné, of days of travel through dense pine woods, or along rushing streams in frail bark canoes. He told of the rapids that seethed in white foam over hidden boulders, where the only thing one could do was to trust to the guidance of the Indian who paddled the boat, and of the crossing from one river to another, when the canoe was beached and carried on the men's shoulders through the forests. There the sunlight played among the trees, and set the autumn leaves ablaze with red and gold, and squirrels chattered and birds sang and the rich scent of pines made one think of the Magi's frankincense offered to the great Lord of all. Those were quiet, peaceful times, the times of portage. But when the next river was reached, and the canoe launched, and the swift stream bore it away, it was a joy to know the end of the journey was drawing nearer.

Mother Duchesne was filled with gratitude for what God was doing among the Indians. Soon, soon, they might be, like her, chosen by Our Lord for His special service. She wrote to Mother Barat, "Are holy persons to be deprived of the blessings of religious life because they have Indian blood in their veins? They are for the most part as intelligent as white people and can arrive at a high degree of sanctity."

She still had the joy of serving God's little ones. It was a special treat for the boarding-school children to be allowed to visit Mother Duchesne; she was so kind and so full of wonderful holiness, that it was enough just to sit and look at her; with her poor chilblained hands hidden in the old mittens, and her patched habit and darned veil and the smile that lit up her face when they spoke to her, she made them think of St Francis of Assisi. They did not always believe her.

"Mother," one child asked her class mistress, "I thought saints always told the truth. Mother Duchesne said to-day she was over eighty and she'd spent over thirty years in America and she'd done very little for the glory of our Master. But that can't be true, can it, because before she came, there weren't any convents of the Sacred Heart and now there are about a dozen in the States and in Canada, and that's her doing, isn't it?"

"She doesn't think it is," the nun answered. "When you've got the clear sight of a saint, you will feel you need a microscope to see any good that you've done."

Léonie Bernard's father had a farm in the neighbourhood. She came each day in his cart to school, and she loved the little lessons the old nun gave them in the day school.

"We've lots of lovely things at the farm," she confided to her, sorry at the thought that Mother Duchesne had only a little garden to walk in and so little to see. "I'll bring you a surprise to-morrow—something that's ever so pretty."

The next day she arrived with a peacock protesting harshly at his confinement in the cart. But his spirits revived when he was set on the green spring grass, and he strutted majestically before the small girl and the aged, bent nun. Feeling the warm sunlight on his back, he slowly opened his tail, and a hundred bright eyes quivered and shone with irridescent colours. As though to display his beauty to the full, he marched along, pausing at intervals to call attention to himself with hoarse screams. Mother Duchesne looked. Somewhere in the back of her mind, old recollections were stirring. Yes, it was St Francis of Sales who had loved to illustrate human faults and qualities by comparison with those of creatures. The peacock—what a proud bird he was! Pride—how ugly in man, in God's image and likeness! All her life she had had to fight her pride, looking to Him who had said, "I am meek and humble of heart. Learn of Me." A life-time spent in learning from the Lamb of God, learning to be led to the slaughter and not to open her mouth, and how imperfect she still was!

The child beside her gazed anxiously up into the quiet wrinkled face.

"Don't you like him, Mother?" she asked, feeling that something had gone wrong.

Mother Duchesne smiled at her.

"God makes lovely things—it's we who spoil them," she mused. "You must have wonderful things at your farm. Have you a lamb?"

"Oh, yes," said Léonie, happy again. "We've lots now, because the winter's gone. You wait."

Back home at the end of the day went the proud peacock. The next day Léonie staggered towards Mother Duchesne with a lamb in her arms. She set him down on the green grass, and he stood on his long legs warming himself for a moment in the sun. Mother Duchesne gave an exclamation of pleasure. The lamb ran across to her.

"He's all white," said Léonie delightedly. "And so warm and woolly."

"And so gentle and loving," said Mother Duchesne, as he rubbed his nose against her hand. "You must go to the kitchen and ask sister there for some milk for him."

"He's for you—for your very own," said Léonie.

Some days later, Mother Duchesne was kneeling as usual motionless before the tabernacle.

"What on earth has she got on her habit?" a sister wondered as she entered the chapel. Curiously she walked up the aisle. There, at rest against the skirts of the old Mother, lay Léonie's lamb.

"It must have followed me in," said Mother Duchesne meekly as the sister stooped and lifted the little white creature. "I'm sorry."

"I guess the Lord isn't," said the sister to herself. "It's the prettiest thing I've seen. If only I could draw—"

Robert, the negro servant at the convent, was eighty, too, but the eyes in his furrowed black face were as sharp as ever they had been.

"What on earth's the matter, Robert?" the sacristy sister asked as she came across him in the passage after Mass. He was waving his arms and talking to himself in a state of great excitement.

"Eh, sister, the matter! Eighty years I've been on this earth and never before to-day have I seen one!"

"One what?"

"Why, one saint. That Mother Duchesne, sister. That's what I'm telling you—she's a saint. I seen it. I seen it with these two eyes of mine."

"Seen what?"

"Why, the light, sister, the heavenly light. Mother Duchesne goes up to the altar. I'm in the side chapel, sister, and I look. Mother Duchesne kneels. Along comes the priest and gives her Holy Communion. Then, quick as a flash of lightning, her face is all shining with light. Like the Blessed Saints in the pictures. You've seen a saint, Robert, I say to myself. A saint all bright and shining."

"God is always good," Mother Duchesne thought with each new day, but she had not looked for the joy He sent her in the spring of 1852. Mother Regis Hamilton came as superior to St Charles, the dearest of her first novices, whose very name spoke of so many shared hopes and loves. This was Mother Barat's doing. Together they looked at the picture of the saint who had watched over Florissant, now honoured anew at St Charles. Her cup of happiness seemed ready to overflow.

Mother Hamilton wrote to Mother Barat: "I care for her, but not as I should wish, for she still has the idea that she must do penance and that everything is too good for her."

Happiness gave a flicker of new life, but on 16 August, Mother Duchesne became so ill that they gave her the Last Sacraments. She rallied, and by the twenty-ninth the danger was past.

"Eighty-three to-day," she thought, facing the possibility of another year of exile. "Perhaps God wants me to wait longer for the joy of seeing Him."

Waiting—she had done much of that in her life. Her waiting had never been perfect, and always, after, she had found that God had given more and better than her impatience had desired. This time she was ready to wait for His sweet pleasure. Though she had to be carried to the chapel, she could still receive Him each morning and spend the rest of the day in thanksgiving and petition.

She was still waiting when the leaves fell from the trees and the cold of winter came. There was another joy that entered into that bleak season. Mother Barat was sending some of her daughters southward to found houses in Peru. No less a person was to go than the Superior of Turin who had been driven from that city by the Revolutionaries. She was now actually in America, visiting houses with the authority of the Mother General.

On 16 November the new Visitatrix, Mother Anna du Rousier, was at St Louis, pleased with all she had seen in the American foundations, pleasing all with her own kindness. As the day advanced, she found a thought haunted her which she could not dismiss. She saw herself a child of twelve again amongst a group of school children in the old monastery at Poitiers and she was listening to a tall, austere-looking nun whose smile spoke of love and whose words inflamed to zeal. And now that same nun was old and feeble and but twenty miles away from her. She must see her without delay.

"But, Mother," the superior of St Louis protested, "you can't set out to-day. Look at the sky. When it's grey and overcast like that, there will be snow. To-morrow or the day after the weather may be more settled."

But Mother du Rousier insisted. Even when the snow began to fall in large wet flakes, she would not be put off. The coachman grumbled as he led out his horses. This Mother from France would know what American weather could do. Soon they were driving through a blinding storm of sleet that bent the trees and lashed against the panes of the carriage and hid all the countryside in a grey mist.

"What a noise it makes!" thought Mother du Rousier. "You would say we were drawing near to some great river that was flowing over boulders with a rushing sound of waters."

Mother Hamilton was surprised to see her visitors. Mother du Rousier wasted no time with her.

"I have come only to see Mother Duchesne," she said.

They led her to the small room where the old missioner lay on her bed, with her rosary slipping through her fingers, and her eyes resting ever and anon on the tiny little statue of Our Lady del Pilar which Mother Barat had given her on the eve of her departure from Paris thirty-four years ago.

"It's Mother du Rousier, come from our Mother," said Mother Hamilton.

Mother Duchesne's weary face lit up. She tried to raise herself.

"Give me a blessing, Mother," she whispered in her faint voice.

With tears in her eyes, Mother du Rousier blessed her.

"But you must bless me, too," she added. She was going southward to that land Mother Duchesne had longed for, of which only a week ago she had written, "If God will leave me long enough on earth, I think I might set foot on Southern America, at Lima, under the protection of my patron Saint, St Rose." Her blessing at least should go. Mother Duchesne's gnarled old hand, thin and light, sought her forehead and with surprising vigour, marked a cross upon it. At the end of her own long life spent for the spread of the love of God, she passed on the pledge of the love of God to this new missioner. With the imprint of that blessing upon her, Mother du Rousier drove back to St Louis through the wind and snow.

Mother Hamilton noticed a change in the invalid on the evening of the seventeenth. It would be safer, she thought, if she herself sat up with her. Mother Duchesne opened her eyes and noticed, and knew what it meant.

"If you do not go to rest, I shall get up," she said, with a flash of her old determination.

A sister came in and for the first time lit a fire in her room.

"You think only of the things of this world," she said,

smilingly. "It would be better to say a *Pater* or an *Ave* for the good of my soul."

She coughed incessantly but would not break her fast by drinking, for fear of losing her Communion. Through the night she kept repeating, "How happy I am to die in this house where charity reigns!"

"Pray that I may die, too," the sister asked.

Again came the old Duchesne vigour.

"Indeed I shall not. What would Reverend Mother do if everyone in the house died?"

There was work always and everywhere for souls. There must be no laggards among the workers.

God had a last joy for this valiant labourer. Fr Verhaegen, passing through St Charles, came to the house and at ten in the morning gave her the Last Anointings with the hands that had so often touched the eyes and ears and nostrils and mouths and hands and feet of the Redskins, and the voice that had bidden their souls go forth on the last journey sounded now in her ears. He had brought her her Lord and Master. What more could she do in this life?

Mother Hamilton knelt beside her.

"You offer your life to God?"

"Oh, yes," she answered at once. "My life—so whole-heartedly."

Waiting surely now was at an end.

"Come, Lord Jesus, and do not delay," she said. "Come quickly."

When the noonday Angelus rang, He had taken her home.

On 20 November her body was laid to rest in the little cemetery in the convent garden. Fr Verhaegen had said the Requiem Mass and followed to the grave. "*In Paradisum*," he thought, as he went back to the sacristy. Within the chapel, the nuns were saying the *De profundis*. He took a pen and wrote the entry of the burial in the register, and added his own tribute: "Eminent in all the virtues of religious life but especially in humility, she sweetly and calmly departed this life in the odour of sanctity on the eighteenth day of November 1852."

He signed his name and went out. The sun was breaking through the grey clouds and sparkled on the Missouri as it flowed down to the Mississippi. He seemed to follow the waters on their thousand-mile course to the ocean where they were caught up, to flow ceaselessly round all the world. The Isère running into the Rhône would mingle its waters, too. God's love was like that—boundless, world embracing. Philippine Duchesne knew that now in all its fullness.